It's another Quality Book from CGP

This book is for anyone doing GCSE Mathematics at Higher Level.

It contains lots of tricky questions designed to
make you sweat — because that's the only
way you'll get any better.

It's also got some daft bits in to try and make
the whole experience at least vaguely
entertaining for you.

What CGP is all about

Our sole aim here at CGP is to produce the highest quality
books — carefully written, immaculately presented
and dangerously close to being funny.

Then we work our socks off to get them out to you
— at the cheapest possible prices.

Published by Coordination Group Publications Ltd.
Illustrated by Lex Ward and Ashley Tyson

Coordinated by June Hall and Mark Haslam

Contributors:
Gill Allen
JE Dodds
Mark Haslam
C McLoughlin
Claire Thompson
John Waller

ISBN 1-84146-009-5

Groovy website: www.cgpbooks.co.uk

Printed by Elanders Hindson, Newcastle upon Tyne.
Clipart sources: CorelDRAW and VECTOR.

With thanks to Colin Wells and Angela Ryder for the proofreading.

Contents

Section One — Number

Questions on Numbers 1
Questions on Decimals 3
Questions on Factors and Primes 4
Questions on Fractions 6
Questions on Rational and Irrational 8
Questions on Percentages 10
Questions on Calculator Buttons 14
Questions on Conversion Factors 16
Questions on Rounding Off 20
Questions on Estimating 22
Questions on Sequences 24

Section Two — Shapes

Questions on Regular Polygons 28
Questions on Areas 30
Questions on Volumes 33
Questions on Loci and Constructions 38
Questions on Geometry 40
Questions on Circle Geometry 44
Questions on Similarity and Enlargement 46
Questions on The Four Transformations 48

Section Three — Bits and Bobs

Questions on Formula Triangles 50
Questions on Speed, Distance and Time 52
Questions on D/T graphs and V/T graphs 54
Questions on Powers and Roots 60
Questions on Pythagoras and Bearings 62
Questions on Trigonometry 65
Questions on The Sine and Cosine Rules 68
Questions on the Graphs of Sin, Cos and Tan 70
Questions on Angles of Any Size 72
Questions on Vectors 74
Questions on Real Life Vectors 76

Section Four — Statistics

Questions on Mean, Median, Mode, Range 78
Questions on Probability 82
Questions on Frequency Tables 86
Questions on Grouped Frequency 88
Questions on Cumulative Frequency 92
Questions on Scatter Graphs and Histograms 96
Questions on Histograms and Dispersion 100
Questions on Stem and Leaf Diagrams 102
Questions on Time Series 103
Questions on Frequency (Mixed) 104
Questions on Sampling Methods 106

Section Five — Graphs

Questions on Straight Lines 108
Questions on Plotting Straight Lines 109
Questions on Y = mX + C 112
Questions on Plotting Curves 114
Questions on Solving Eq's Using Graphs 115
Questions on Tangents and Gradient 118
Questions on Graphs to Recognise 121
Questions on Equations from Graphs 124
Questions on Area 127
Questions on Linear Programming 128
Questions on Transforming Graphs 130
Questions on Uses of Coordinates 132

Section Six — Lovely Algebra

Questions on The Basics 133
Questions on Algebraic Fractions 135
Questions on Solving Equations 137
Questions on Rearranging Formulas 139
Questions on Inequalities 141
Questions on Direct & Inverse Proportion 143
Questions on Factorising Quadratics 145
Questions on The Quadratic Formula 147
Questions on Completing the Square 149
Questions on Trial and Improvement 150
Questions on Growth and Decay 153
Questions on Simultaneous Equations 154
Questions on Simultaneous Eq' Graphs 156

1.1   Questions on Numbers

Q1   Sarah thinks of a number. She calculates that the square of the number is 256. What is the square root of the number?

Q2   Mr Harris had a party. He bought 50 bottles of lemonade costing 75p each and some bottles of orange juice costing 82p each. Altogether he spent £71.94. How many bottles of orange juice did he buy?

Q3   A wheel is rotating at the rate of 20 revolutions per minute.
     a) How many revolutions does it make in 2 hours?
     b) How long will it take to make 1000 revolutions?

Q4   On a certain day the temperature at midday was 14°C. By midnight the temperature had fallen by 17°C. What was the temperature at midnight?

 There are five special number sequences that you really need to know: **EVEN, ODD, SQUARE, CUBE** *and* **TRIANGLE NUMBERS.**

Q5   The number one is the first odd number. It is also the first square number, the first cube number and the first triangle number.
     a) Which is greater: the third odd number, the third square number or the third cube number?
     b) Write down the prime factors of the third triangle number.

Q6   The following sequences are described in words. Write down their first four terms.
     a) The prime numbers starting from 17.
     b) The squares of odd numbers starting from $9^2 = 81$.
     c) The triangular numbers starting from 15.

Remember — 1 is not a prime. Look, it just isn't, OK.

Q7   Using any or all of the figures **1, 2, 5, 9** write down:
     a) the smallest prime number
     b) a prime number greater than 20
     c) a prime number between 10 and 20
     d) two prime numbers whose sum is 21
     e) a number that is not prime.

Q8   **a)** In the ten by ten square opposite, ring all the <u>prime numbers</u>. (The first three have been done for you.)
     b) Among the prime numbers between 10 and 100, find three which are still prime when their digits are reversed.
     c) Give a reason for 27 not being a prime number.

1	②	③	4	⑤	6	7	8	9	10
11	12	13	14	15	16	17	18	19	20
21	22	23	24	25	26	27	28	29	30
31	32	33	34	35	36	37	38	39	40
41	42	43	44	45	46	47	48	49	50
51	52	53	54	55	56	57	58	59	60
61	62	63	64	65	66	67	68	69	70
71	72	73	74	75	76	77	78	79	80
81	82	83	84	85	86	87	88	89	90
91	92	93	94	95	96	97	98	99	100

Q9   What is the largest prime less than 300?

Q10   How many prime numbers are even?

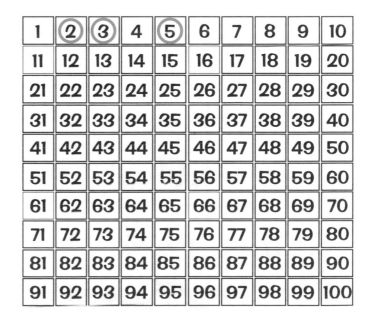

This stuff <u>keeps coming up</u> in the Exam — so make sure you can check if a number's prime or not. It's actually dead easy — check out the method in The Revision Guide.

1.1 *Questions on Numbers*

Q11 Find three sets of three prime numbers which add up to the following numbers:
22   47   91

Q12 Alice, Ronan and Sarah regularly go swimming. Alice goes every 2 days, Ronan goes every 3 days and Sarah goes every 5 days. They <u>all</u> went swimming together on Friday 1st June.

  a) On what <u>date</u> will Alice and Ronan next go swimming together?

  b) On what <u>date</u> will Ronan and Sarah next go swimming together?

  c) On what <u>day of the week</u> will all 3 next go swimming together?

  d) Which of the 3 (if any) will go swimming on 15th June?

Q13 Giving your answer as a fraction in its <u>lowest terms</u>, what fraction of each shape is shaded?

  a)

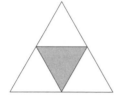

  b)

  c)

  d)

Q14 Billy spent £5.25 on three items at the chemist's. He bought a Cutthroat Razor which cost twice as much as the dirty face soap he bought, which cost twice as much as his Greasy Hair Gel. How much did the gel cost?

Q15 Using the diagram, work out the total cost of buying one tomato, one cucumber and a lettuce.

1.2 Questions on Decimals

Q1 Write the following fractions as decimals:

a) $\dfrac{3}{10}$ b) $\dfrac{37}{100}$ c) $\dfrac{2}{5}$ d) $\dfrac{3}{8}$ e) $\dfrac{14}{8}$

Q2 Write down:

a) 33.9×10 c) 2.3902×1000 e) 122.6×100

b) 0.32×100 d) 64.9×10 f) 5.29×1000

You just shift the decimal point along... this is too easy.

Q3 Calculate:

a) $8.38 + 8.46$ d) $5.79 - 0.98$ g) $1.84 + 8.61 + 5.6$

b) $14.77 + 0.13$ e) $109.79 - 68.32$ h) $(1.40 - 0.29) - 7.33$

c) $4.83 + 35.32$ f) $1.22 - 3.40$ i) $7.33 + 59.2 - 34.2$

Q4 Work out:

a) 6.75×5 d) $6.75 \div 5$ g) $5 \times 6.2 \times 3.9$

b) 3.59×3.8 e) $6.25 \div 2.5$ h) $(2.5 \div 5) \div 0.1$

c) 8.05×111.11 f) $4.29 \div 0.066$ i) $1.6 \times 0.4 \div 0.2$

Q5 Terri's motorbike travels 122.5 km on 3.5 litres of petrol.

a) How many kilometres per litre is this?

b) How far can Terri travel on 0.3 litres of petrol?

c) How much petrol does Terri need to travel 7 km?

Decimals are just another way of writing fractions — so it's easy to convert between the two...

Q6 In the following conversion table fill in the gaps:

Fraction	Decimal
½	0.5
⅕	
	0.125
	1.6
⁴⁄₁₆	
⁷⁄₂	
	0.x
ˣ⁄₁₀₀	
³⁄₂₀	
	0.45

Q7 Write the following percentages as decimals:

a) 75%   b) 30%   c) 15.5%   d) 12%   e) 89.42%

I reckon swapping between decimals and percentages is about as good as it gets — make the most of it.

Q8 Fill in the gaps in the conversion table:

All you do is multiply or divide by 100 — couldn't be easier.

Decimal	Percentage
	25%
0.4	
0.22	
0.0x	
	15%
	89%
1.0	
	67%
0.x	
	78.2%

1.3 *Questions on Factors and Primes*

Q1   1   3   6   9   12

From the numbers above, write down:

a) a multiple of 4

b) the prime number

c) two square numbers

d) three factors of 27.

e) two numbers P and Q that satisfy both $P = 2Q$ and $P = \sqrt{144}$.

This is real basic stuff — you just have to know your times tables. And your primes, of course...

Q2 **a)** Find the lowest common multiple of 5 and 9.

b) Find the lowest common multiple of 4 and 6.

c) Find the lowest common multiple of 4, 6 and 8.

d) Find the highest common factor of 26 and 52.

e) Find the highest common factor of 26, 39 and 52.

Q3 **a)** Write down the first ten triangle numbers.

b) From your list pick out all multiples of 2.

c) From your list pick out all multiples of 3.

d) From your list pick out any prime numbers.

e) Add the numbers in your list together and write down the prime factorisation of the total.

Q4   Gordon is doing some woodwork and needs to calculate the volume of a wooden rectangular block (cuboid). The length of the block is 50 cm, the height 25 cm and the width 16 cm.

a) What is the volume (in cm³) of the wooden block?

b) What is the prime factorisation of the number found in part **a)**?

Gordon needs to cut the block into smaller blocks with dimensions 4 cm × 5 cm × 5 cm.

c) What is the maximum number of small blocks Gordon can make from the larger block?

The clue's in the question...

Q5   From this list of numbers: 17, 125, 9, 16, 25, 31, 49, 64 write down:

a) all the prime numbers

b) all the odd numbers

c) all the square numbers

d) all the numbers that are odd *and* square.

Q6   A school ran 3 evening classes: Conversational French, Cake Making and Woodturning. The Conversational French class had 29 pupils, Cake Making had 27 pupils, and the Woodturning class had 23. For which classes did the teacher have difficulty dividing the pupils into equal groups?

1.3   Questions on Factors and Primes

Q7 **a)** Write down the first five cube numbers.
   b) Which of the numbers given in part **a)** are multiples of 2?
   c) Which of the numbers given in part **a)** are multiples of 3?
   d) Which of the numbers given in part **a)** are multiples of 4?
   e) Which of the numbers given in part **a)** are multiples of 5?

Q8 Express the following as a product of prime factors:
   a) 18
   b) 140
   c) 47.

The tricky bit is remembering that a <u>prime factorisation</u> includes <u>all</u> the factors that multiply to make that number — so you've got to repeat some of them.

Q9 The prime factorisation of a certain number is $3^2 \times 5 \times 11$.
   a) Write down the number.
   b) Write down the prime factorisation of 165.

Q10 **a)** List the first five prime numbers.
   b) If added together, what is their total?
   c) Write down the prime factorisation of the answer to part **b)**.

Q11 The prime factorisation of a certain number is $2^3 \times 5 \times 17$.
   a) What is the number?
   b) What is the prime factorisation of half of this number?
   c) What is the prime factorisation of a quarter of the number?
   d) What is the prime factorisation of an eighth of the number?

Q12 **a)** List the first five odd numbers.
   b) If added together, what is their total?
   c) Write down the prime factorisation of the answer to part **b)**.

Q13 Bryan and Sue were playing a guessing game. Sue thought of a number between 1 and 100 which Bryan had to guess. Bryan was allowed to ask five questions, which are listed with Sue's responses in the table below.

Bryan's Questions	Sue's Responses
Is it prime?	No
Is it odd?	No
Is it less than 50?	Yes
Is it a multiple of 3?	Yes
Is it a multiple of 7?	Yes

Start by writing down a number table up to 100. Look at each response in turn and cross off numbers 'till you've only got one left.

What is the number that Sue thought of?

1.4   *Questions on Fractions*

Q1   Evaluate the following, giving your answer as a fraction in its lowest terms:

a) $\dfrac{1}{8} + \dfrac{1}{8}$ c) $\dfrac{3}{18} + \dfrac{1}{3}$ e) $1\dfrac{1}{4} + 4\dfrac{1}{8}$

b) $\dfrac{1}{6} + \dfrac{2}{3}$ d) $1\dfrac{1}{4} + 3\dfrac{1}{8}$ f) $\dfrac{9}{10} + \dfrac{9}{100} + \dfrac{1}{100}$

Q2   Evaluate the following, giving your answer as a fraction in its lowest terms:

a) $\dfrac{1}{8} - \dfrac{1}{8}$ c) $\dfrac{3}{18} - \dfrac{1}{3}$ e) $1\dfrac{1}{8} - 4\dfrac{1}{4}$

b) $\dfrac{2}{3} - \dfrac{1}{6}$ d) $3\dfrac{1}{8} - 1\dfrac{1}{4}$ f) $\left(\dfrac{9}{10} - \dfrac{9}{100}\right) - \dfrac{1}{100}$

Q3   Carry out the following multiplications, giving your answer as a fraction in its lowest terms:

a) $\dfrac{1}{8} \times \dfrac{1}{8}$ c) $\dfrac{3}{18} \times \dfrac{1}{3}$ e) $1\dfrac{1}{4} \times 4\dfrac{1}{8}$

b) $\dfrac{2}{3} \times \dfrac{1}{6}$ d) $1\dfrac{1}{4} \times 3\dfrac{1}{8}$ f) $\dfrac{9}{10} \times \dfrac{9}{100} \times \dfrac{1}{100}$

Q4   Carry out the following divisions, giving your answer as a fraction in its lowest terms:

a) $\dfrac{1}{8} \div \dfrac{1}{8}$ c) $\dfrac{3}{18} \div \dfrac{1}{3}$ e) $1\dfrac{1}{4} \div 4\dfrac{1}{8}$

b) $\dfrac{2}{3} \div \dfrac{1}{6}$ d) $1\dfrac{1}{4} \div 3\dfrac{1}{8}$ f) $\left(\dfrac{9}{10} \div \dfrac{9}{100}\right) \div \dfrac{1}{100}$

Q5   Evaluate the following, giving your answer as a fraction in its lowest terms:

a) $\dfrac{1}{2} + \dfrac{1}{4}$ e) $6 \times \dfrac{2}{3}$ i) $3 + \dfrac{8}{5}$

b) $\dfrac{2}{3} - \dfrac{1}{4}$ f) $\dfrac{4}{5} \div \dfrac{2}{3}$ j) $\dfrac{2}{3}\left(\dfrac{3}{4} + \dfrac{4}{5}\right)$

c) $\dfrac{1}{5} + \dfrac{2}{3} - \dfrac{2}{5}$ g) $\dfrac{5}{12} \times \dfrac{3}{2}$ k) $\left(\dfrac{1}{7} + \dfrac{3}{14}\right) \times \left(3 - \dfrac{1}{5}\right)$

d) $5 - \dfrac{1}{4}$ h) $\dfrac{5}{6} - \dfrac{7}{8}$ l) $\left(\dfrac{3}{4} - \dfrac{1}{5}\right) \div \left(\dfrac{7}{8} + \dfrac{1}{16}\right)$

Q6   Dwight scored 50 goals last season, 30 of these were scored at his home ground.
a) Write down the fraction (in its lowest terms) of goals scored at his home ground.
b) Calculate the fraction of goals scored away from home.

Don't forget to make the bottom numbers the same when adding (or subtracting) fractions... it's all a bit of a breeze, really.

1.4   *Questions on Fractions*

Q7   A ball is dropped from a height of 6 m.

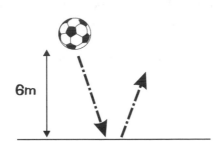

6m

This stuff is pretty easy — but you don't want to go making silly mistakes in the exam. Get the practice in now.

After each bounce the ball rises to 2/3 of its previous height. What height will it reach after the third bounce?

Q8   George wants to make a cake. The recipe requires 150 g each of flour, sugar and butter, and 3 eggs. George only has 2 eggs so he decides to make a smaller cake with the same proportions.

a) How much flour will George need to use?

b) If each egg weighs 25 g, how much will the cake weigh before it goes in the oven?

c) What fraction of the uncooked weight is flour?

d) If the cake loses 1/7 of its weight during baking (due to moisture loss) what will it weigh after baking?

Q9   The population of Australia is 18 million, of which 3.5 million people live in Sydney and 1 million people live in Perth.

a) What fraction of the population live in Perth?

b) What fraction of the population live in Perth or Sydney?

Q10   Green Island is split into six regions A, B, C, D, E and F. The areas of the six regions are 12, 2, 3, 18, 4, and 9 km² respectively.

a) What is the total area of the island?

b) What fraction of the island's area is taken up by the two largest regions?

Q11   In a consumer survey, 100 people stated their favourite vegetable. 25 people chose peas, 35 carrots and 32 runner beans.

a) How many of the 100 people chose a vegetable other than peas, carrots or runner beans?

b) What fraction of the 100 people chose carrots as their favourite vegetable?

c) What fraction of the 100 people chose peas as their favourite vegetable?

d) At least how many people chose a green vegetable as their favourite?

e) Not more than how many people chose a green vegetable as their favourite?

1.5 Questions on Rational and Irrational

Well, to be honest, I think the idea of rational and irrational numbers is a bit odd. Basically, a <u>rational</u> number is either a <u>whole</u> number or one you can write as a <u>fraction</u>. An <u>irrational</u> number... you guessed it... is <u>not</u> whole and <u>can't</u> be written as a fraction.

Q1 Write down a rational number and an irrational number both greater than $\sqrt{5}$ and less than 5.

Q2 **a)** Define what is meant by a rational number.
b) Using your definition show that P^2 is a rational number whenever P is a rational number.

Q3 Give an example of two different irrational numbers, x and y, where x/y is a rational number.

Q4 Write down a value of x for which $x^{\frac{1}{2}}$ is:
a) irrational
b) rational.

―Watch out for those square― ― and cube roots — they're ― ―sometimes a bit irrational...―

Q5 Which of the following powers of $\sqrt{3}$ are rational and which are irrational:

a) $(\sqrt{3})^1$ **c)** $(\sqrt{3})^3$

b) $(\sqrt{3})^2$ **d)** $(\sqrt{3})^4$

Q6 P is a rational number and Q is an irrational number. Give a value for P and a corresponding value for Q such that $P+Q = \sqrt{5}$.

Q7 Five of the following numbers are rational and five are irrational:

$\sqrt{2} \times \sqrt{8}$, $(\sqrt{5})^6$, $\sqrt{3}/\sqrt{2}$, $(\sqrt{7})^3$, 6π, 0.4, $\sqrt{5} - 2.1$, $40 - 2^{-1} - 4^{-2}$, $49^{-\frac{1}{2}}$, $\sqrt{6} + 6$

a) Write down the five rational numbers.
b) Write down the five irrational numbers.

Q8 **a)** Write down a rational number which is greater than 1 but less than 2.
b) Write down an irrational number which lies between 1 and 2.
c) If P is a non-zero rational number, is 1/P also a rational number? Clearly show your reasoning.

Q9 Which of the following are rational and which are irrational?

a) $16^{\frac{1}{2}}$ **b)** $16^{\frac{1}{3}}$ **c)** $16^{\frac{1}{4}}$

Q10 Write down an irrational value of x for which x^{-2} is:
a) irrational
b) rational.

Q11 P and Q are two irrational numbers. Give a value for P and a corresponding value for Q such that PQ = 6.

― Don't forget that recurring decimals, like ― 0.333333333, can be put into fraction ― form, like $\frac{1}{3}$, — so they're rational too.―

1.5 Questions on Rational and Irrational

Q12 Show clearly why 4.262626... is a rational number.

Q13 If $x=2$, $y=\sqrt{3}$ and $z=2\sqrt{2}$, which of the following expressions are rational and which are irrational? (show working)

a) xyz

b) $(xyz)^2$

c) $x + yz$

d) $\dfrac{yz}{2\sqrt{3x}}$

Q14 Are the following expressions rational or irrational?

a) $(1+\sqrt{5})(1-\sqrt{5})$

b) $\dfrac{1+\sqrt{5}}{1-\sqrt{5}}$

Q15 If $x = 1$ and $y = \sqrt{2}$, are the following expressions rational or irrational?

a) $(x+y)(x-y)$

b) $\dfrac{x+y}{x-y}$

Q16 Show clearly why 1.3434... is a rational number.

Q17 Write down a rational and an irrational number which lie between $\sqrt{2}$ and π.

Q18 If P is a non-zero rational number show that $(P+1)$ is also a rational number.

Q19 If $x=2\sqrt{5}$, $y=5$ and $z=5\sqrt{2}$, which of the following expressions are rational and which are irrational? (show working)

a) x^5

b) x^2yz^2

c) $x\sqrt{5}$

d) $xy + z^2$

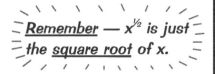
Remember — $x^{1/2}$ is just the square root of x.

Q20 P and Q are two rational numbers. Give a value for P and a corresponding value for Q such that $P^{1/2}Q = \tfrac{1}{2}$.

Q21 Give an example of two different irrational numbers, x and y, where xy is a rational number.

Q22 Dennis draws a right angled triangle. Using Pythagoras' theorem he works out that the length of the hypotenuse is $\sqrt{2}$. Is sin (45°) rational or irrational?

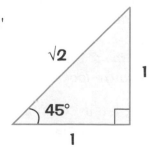

1.6   *Questions on Percentages*

Make sure you can switch from fractions to decimals to percentages
before you start.

Q1   Express each percentage as a decimal:

   a) 50%   **b)** 12%   **c)** 40%   **d)** 34%

Q2   Express each percentage as a fraction in its lowest terms:

   a) 25%   **b)** 60%   **c)** 45%   **d)** 30%

Q3   Express each of the following as a percentage:

   a) $\dfrac{1}{8}$ **b)** 0.23   **c)** $\dfrac{12}{40}$ **d)** 0.34

Q4   In a French test Lauren scored 17/20. What percentage is this?

Q5   87 out of 120 pupils at Backwater School have access to a computer. What percentage is this?

There are three types of percentage question — and working out
"something % of something else" is dead easy. Just remember to add
it back on to the original amount if you've got a V.A.T. question.

Oh look...

Q6

> **Bed and breakfast £37 per person**
> **Evening meal £15 per person**

Four friends stay at the Pickled Parrot Hotel for a night and
each take an evening meal. How much is the total cost, if
VAT is added at 17½%?

Q7   John bought a new video recorder. The tag in the shop said it cost £299 + VAT. If VAT is charged at 17½%, how much did he pay (to the nearest penny)?

Q8   Donald earns an annual wage of £23,500. He doesn't pay tax on the first £3400 that he earns. How much income tax does he pay when the rate of tax is:

   a) 25%

   b) 40%?

Q9   Tanya paid £6500 for her new car. Each year its value decreased by 8%.

   a) How much was it worth when it was one year old?

   b) How much was it worth when it was two years old?

Here's the 2nd type — finding "something as a percentage of something else" — in this
case you're looking at percentage change, so don't forget to work that out first.

Q10   During a rain storm a water butt increased its weight from 10.4 kg to 13.6 kg. What was the percentage increase (to the nearest percent)?

1.6 Questions on Percentages

Q11 There are approximately 6000 Fish and Chip Shops in the UK. On average, a Fish and Chip Shop gets about 160 visitors each day. Given that the population of the UK is roughly 60 million, approximately what percentage of the population visit a Fish and Chip Shop each day?

Q12 An electrical store reduces the price of a particular camera from £90.00 to £78.30. What is the percentage reduction (to 1 d.p.)?

Q13 If L = MN, what is the percentage increase in L if M increases by 15% and N increases by 20%?

Q14 On 1 November 1973 Mr Short borrowed £120 from his bank. He repaid £32 on 31 October 1974 and the same amount on the same date each year thereafter. Compound interest was charged at 14% per annum on the balance during the year. How much did he still owe on 1 November 1976?

Q15 Springtown College runs an evening class for mature students wanting to learn German. A week before their final examination the students take a mock exam. The results of the mock exam and the final examination for the 32 students are shown below.

		Final Exam	
		Pass	Fail
Mock Exam	Pass	20	2
	Fail	4	6

a) What percentage of the students passed the final exam?
b) What percentage of the students had their final examination result correctly predicted by the mock exam?

Ooh... here's the 3rd type — finding the original value. The bit most people get wrong is deciding whether the value given represents more or less than 100% of the original — so always check your answer makes sense.

Q16 In the new year sales Robin bought a tennis racket for £68.00. The original price had been reduced by 15%. What was the original price?

Q17 There were 300 people living in a certain village a year ago. Today the population of the village is 360.
a) What is the annual percentage increase in the population?
b) How many whole years from today will it be before the population has more than doubled from it's current size?

1.6   Questions on Percentages

Yet more percentages. They really want you to know this stuff, so you need to practise.

Q18   I wish to invest £1000 for a period of three years and have decided to place my money with the Highrise Building Society on 1 January. If I choose to use the Gold Account I will withdraw the interest at the end of each year. If I choose to use the Silver Account I will leave the interest to be added to the capital at the end of each year.

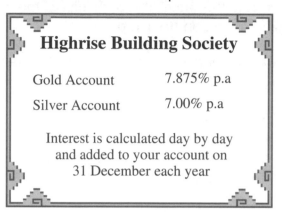

Highrise Building Society

Gold Account   7.875% p.a

Silver Account   7.00% p.a

Interest is calculated day by day
and added to your account on
31 December each year

a) Calculate the total interest I will receive if I use the Gold Account.

b) Calculate the total interest I will receive if I use the Silver Account.

After some thought I decide to use the Gold Account and leave the interest to be added to the capital at the end of each year.

c) Calculate the total interest I will now receive from the Gold Account.

Q19   In a crossword, Martha knew 16/25 of the answers. What percentage is this?

Q20   In a survey 152/190 people said they could speak no foreign languages. What percentage is this?

Q21   A sign in a camping supplies shop window said that a deluxe tent was only £150.50. After negotiating with the shop manager I managed to get a 5% reduction on the price. How much did I pay for my deluxe tent?

Q22   Jeremy wanted a new sofa for his lounge. A local furniture shop had just what he was looking for — and for only £130.00 + VAT. Jeremy had £150 pounds in his bank account. If VAT was charged at 17½% could Jeremy afford the sofa?

Q23   Jane earns £16500 a year before tax. She doesn't pay tax on the first £2800 that she earns. How much income tax does she pay a year when the rate of tax is:

a) 20%

b) 35%?

Crikey — you're gonna be well sick of these by the time you've finished.

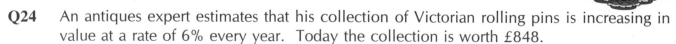

Q24   An antiques expert estimates that his collection of Victorian rolling pins is increasing in value at a rate of 6% every year. Today the collection is worth £848.

a) How much was his collection worth a year ago?

b) How much will his collection be worth one year from now?

1.6   *Questions on Percentages*

 Look out for words like increase, decrease, profit, loss, error, improvement, discount — they usually mean a "percentage change" question...

Q25   At birth, Veronica was 0.3 m tall. By adulthood she had grown to 1.5 m tall. Calculate her height now as a percentage of her height at birth.

Q26   If $L = M^2$, what is the percentage increase in L if M increases by 10%?

Q27   On 1 January 1952 Mr Cash borrowed £50 from his bank. He repaid £9 on 31 December 1952 and the same amount on the same date each year thereafter. Compound interest was charged at 29% per annum on the balance during the year. Did he still owe money to the bank on 1 January 1983?

Q28   Clive bought a new hat in the sales for £18.00. The original price had been reduced by 25%. What was the original price?

Q29   There are approximately 13000 garden centres in the UK. On average, 520 people visit one each week. Given that the population of the UK is roughly 60 million, approximately what percentage of the population visit a garden centre each week?

Q30   A DIY shop reduces the price of a standard wooden gate from £42.00 to £27.00. What is the percentage reduction?

Q31   Rockwood School's results for 'A' level biology are given in the table below.

Results for A level Biology	
Grade	Number of passes
A	4
B	6
C	7
D	4
E	3
Other	2

    a) What percentage of candidates achieved grade A?
    b) What percentage of candidates achieved either grade A, B or C?
    c) What percentage of candidates didn't achieve either grade A, B or C?

Q32   Desmond's GCSE maths exam is next week. As part of his revision he attempted 31 questions on his least favourite topic of percentages. He got 21 questions fully right on the first attempt. Two days later he tried all 31 questions again and this time got 29 correct.

    a) What percentage of questions did he get correct on his first attempt?
    b) What percentage of question did he get correct on his second attempt?
    c) What is the percentage improvement in Desmond's results?
    d) And do you reckon Desmond would have got this question right?

1.7   *Questions on Calculator Buttons*

Q1   Using the x^2 button on your calculator, work out:

   a) 1^2 **d)** 16^2 **g)** $(-5)^2$

   b) 2^2 **e)** $(-1)^2$ **h)** 1000^2

   c) 11^2 **f)** 30^2 **i)** 0^2

        (For parts **e)** and **g)** use your $(-)$ button)

Q2   Using the $\sqrt{}$ button on your calculator, work out:

   a) $\sqrt{16}$ **d)** $\sqrt{0}$ **g)** $\sqrt{3}$

   b) $\sqrt{36}$ **e)** $\sqrt{3600}$ **h)** $\sqrt{7}$

   c) $\sqrt{289}$ **f)** $\sqrt{400}$ **i)** $\sqrt{30}$

Q3   For his birthday Lars Larson was given a new calculator. He pressed the button 2 and then he pressed x^2 and then $=$. He then pressed the Ans button and the x^2 button, then the $=$ button 8 more times. Much to Lars' alarm, a message appeared in the display. What was the message and why did it appear?

Q4   Use the $\sqrt[3]{}$ button on your calculator to work out:

   a) $\sqrt[3]{1}$ **e)** $\sqrt[3]{27}$ *Yeah, OK, we all know how to do sums on*

   b) $\sqrt[3]{0}$ **f)** $\sqrt[3]{-27}$ *a calculator — but it can do so much*

                                              more... check out the groovy powers

   c) $\sqrt[3]{343}$ **g)** $\sqrt[3]{-64}$ *button and the funky brackets buttons,*

   d) $\sqrt[3]{1000}$ **h)** $\sqrt[3]{-5}$ *not to mention the slinky $1/x$ button...*

Q5   By calculating the bottom line first (the denominator) and then using your calculator's memory buttons, work out:

   a) $\dfrac{21}{2+\sin 30°}$ **c)** $\dfrac{15}{\cos 30°+22}$ **e)** $\dfrac{12}{12+\tan 60°}$

   b) $\dfrac{\tan 15°}{12+12^2}$ **d)** $\dfrac{18}{3+\sqrt[3]{12}}$ **f)** $\dfrac{18}{11+\tan 77°}$

Q6   Using $[(\text{---}$ and $\text{---})]$ in an appropriate manner calculate:

                                                                  Here comes BODMAS...

   a) $\dfrac{(14+18)}{(2\times 8)}$ **c)** $\dfrac{(9+(4\div 2))}{(11\times 3)}$ **e)** $\dfrac{12}{(8+9)(13-11)}$

   b) $\dfrac{8}{(1\times 4)(8-6)}$ **d)** $\dfrac{14(4\times 8)}{(6+9)}$ **f)** $\dfrac{7(5+4)}{12(9\times 8)}$

1.7   Questions on Calculator Buttons

Q7   Using the $\boxed{x^y}$ button, find:

a) 2^0 d) π^2 g) $(\cos30°)^5$

b) 4^{10} e) e^3 h) 4.29^7

c) 2^{20} f) 3^{10} i) $(\sin45°)^4$

Q8   Using the $\boxed{\text{EXP}}$ or $\boxed{\text{EE}}$ button on your calculator, enter the following numbers into your calculator and write down what you get:

a) 2×10^4

b) 3×10^5

c) 6.29×10^4

Remember — when you use the standard form button, your calculator gives you the answer as 2.3⁴³, when it really means 2.3×10^{43}. It's up to you to write it in the correct form, or your answer will be wrong.

Q9   Work out (leaving your answer in standard form):

a) $\dfrac{2\times10^3}{5\times10^2}$ c) $\dfrac{1.88\times10^3}{9.4\times10^2}$ e) $\dfrac{7.1\times10^3}{3.52\times10^3}$

b) $\dfrac{5.6\times10^4}{2.8\times10^5}$ d) $\dfrac{4.2\times10^9}{3.9\times10^2}$ f) $(8.92\times10^6)\times(1.22\times10^2)$

Number Crossword

ACROSS

1) An imperial length. (4)

5) π is not this kind of number. (8)

7) Centre pages? (11)

9) The _____ of 24 are 1, 2, 3, 4, 6, 12, and 24. (7)

DOWN

2) 2 points in a game of rugby, but these are also required to find the equivalent reading of Celsius from Fahrenheit, hours from minutes, for example. (10)

3) I am divisible only by myself and one. (5)

4) You may add and subtract these where they share a common denominator. (9)

6) Not just guess work you know. (8)

8) I'm irrational but not absurd. (5)

1.8   Questions on Conversion Factors

You've got to know all the metric and imperial conversion factors — there's no way out of it, you'll just have to sit down and learn them, sorry and all that...

Q1   Express the given quantity in terms of the unit(s) in brackets:

a) 2 m [cm]   g) 87 in [ft and in]   m) 6 ft [in]   s) 8 cm 6 mm [mm]

b) 3.3 cm [mm]   h) 43 oz [lb and oz]   n) 5 lb [oz]   t) 3 ft 6 in [in]

c) 4k g [g]   i) 650 m [km]   o) 301 ft [yd and ft] u) 4 lb 7 oz [oz]

d) 600 g [kg]   j) 9 kg [g]   p) 6 m [mm]   v) 550 kg [t]

e) 4 ft [in]   k) 7 g [kg]   q) 2 t [kg]   w) 3 m 54 cm [cm]

f) 36 in [ft]   l) 950 g [kg]   r) 3000 g [kg]   x) 0.7cm [mm]

Q2   Deborah weighs 9 stones 4 pounds.
There are 14 pounds in a stone and 1 kilogram is equal to 0.157 stones.
Change Deborah's weight into kilograms.

Q3   A horse's drinking trough holds 14 gallons of water. How many litres is this?

Q4   Convert 147 g into ounces.

Q5   Barbara cycled 51 km in one day while Barry cycled 30 miles. Who cycled further?

Q6   A pile of bricks weighs 7 tonnes, how many tons is this?

Q7   A seamstress needs to cut an 11 inch strip of finest Chinese silk.
a) How many cm is this?
b) How many mm is this?

Q8   At the gym Arnold can lift a barbell weighing 60 kg.
a) Convert this into lbs.
b) How many ounces is this?
   Sylvester can lift a barbell weighing 0.059 tonnes.
c) Who can lift the most?

Q9   One local garage prices its unleaded petrol at £3.13 per gallon. A supermarket garage prices its unleaded petrol at 67.9p per litre. Which is better value?

Q10   Giles is walking in the mountains with 15 of his friends. He has a gigantic flask containing 12 pints of tea in his back-pack.
a) How many litres of tea is this?
b) If divided equally, how many pints of tea is this per person in the group?
c) How many litres of tea does each person get?

Q11   A recipe for The World's Wobbliest Jelly requires 5 lb of sugar. How many 1 kg bags of sugar does Dick need to buy so that he can make a jelly?

1.8 Questions on Conversion Factors

Q12 Neil is going to buy some fabric for a new pair of trousers that he is going to make. A local shop prices the fabric that he would like at £9.84 per square yard. A fabric superstore prices the same fabric at £10.80 per square metre. According to price, where should Neil buy his fabric?

Q13 The priceless Greek statue in my garden is 21 feet tall.

a) How many inches is this?
b) How many yards is this?
c) How many metres is this?

d) How many cm is this?
e) How many mm is this?
f) How many km is this?

I'm sure you know the difference between 12 and 24 hour clocks, but just so there's no excuses...

Q14 The times below are given using a 24 hour system. Using am or pm, give the equivalent time for a 12 hour clock.

a) 0500
b) 1448

c) 0316
d) 1558

e) 2230
f) 0001

Q15 The times below are taken from a 12 hour clock. Give the equivalent 24 hour readings.

a) 11.30 pm
b) 10.22 am

c) 12.15 am
d) 12.15 pm

e) 8.30 am
f) 4.45 pm

Q16 Find the time elapsed between the following pairs of times:
a) 0820 on 1 October 1999 and 1620 on the same day
b) 10.22 pm on 1 October 1999 and 8.22 am the next day
c) 2.18 am on 1 October 1999 and 2.14 pm later the same day
d) 0310 on 1 October 1999 and 0258 on 3 October 1999.

Q17 Convert the following into hours and minutes:

a) 3.25 hours   b) 0.4 hours   c) 7.3 hours   d) 1.2 hours.

Q18 Convert the following into just hours:
a) 2 hours and 20 minutes
b) 3 hours and 6 minutes
c) 20 minutes.

There's a button on your calc for this, by the way... but practise doing them under your own steam first.

1.8 Questions on Conversion Factors

Q19 This timetable refers to three trains that travel from Asham to Derton.

a) Which train takes longest to get from Asham to Derton?

b) Which train takes longest to get from Cottingham to Derton?

c) I live in Bordhouse. It takes me 8 minutes to walk to the train station. At what time must I leave the house by to arrive in Derton before 1200?

Asham – Derton			
	Train 1	Train 2	Train 3
Asham	0832	1135	1336
Bordhouse	0914	1216	1414
Cottingham	1002	1259	1456
Derton	1101	1404	1602

Q20 The Bon Voyage Holiday Company are offering an exchange rate of 176 Spanish Pesetas for £1 Sterling. They are also offering 7.54 French Francs for £1 Sterling and 2232 Italian Lira also for £1 Sterling. Calculate, to the nearest penny, the Sterling equivalent of:

a) 220 French Francs

b) 6866 Italian Lira

c) 1233 Spanish Pesetas

d) 4400 Spanish Pesetas

e) 11 French Francs

f) 20,900 Italian Lira

g) 5456 Italian Lira

h) 1024 Spanish Pesetas

i) 931 French Francs

j) 390 Spanish Pesetas

k) 14 French Francs

l) 1 Italian Lira.

Remember — multiply and divide then choose your answer.

Using the same exchange rates, convert the following amounts into French Francs:

m) £400

n) 600 Italian Lira

o) 700 Spanish Peseta

p) 3323 Italian Lira.

Again, using the same exchange rates, convert the following amounts into Italian Lira:

q) £50

r) 579 French Francs

s) 70 Spanish Pesetas

t) 60 French Francs.

Q21 Jerry is going on a Moose Spotting trip to Sweden.
He exchanges £500 into Swedish Krona at a rate of £1 = SKr 10.35.

a) How many Swedish Krona does he receive?
At the last minute the trip is cancelled, so Jerry exchanges the Swedish Krona back into pounds and pence. The exchange rate is now £1 = SKr 10.75.

b) Does Jerry make a profit or a loss?

c) To the nearest penny, how much money does Jerry gain/lose?

1.8   *Questions on Conversion Factors*

Q22

| 1 pint=0.568 litres |
| £1=$1.42 |

Which is better value, 2 pints of beer for $5.76 or 1 litre of beer for £3.92?

Q23   Use the conversion graph below to find:

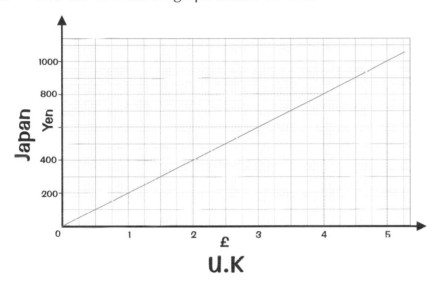

a) £4 in Japanese Yen
b) £3.50 in Japanese Yen
c) £2.25 in Japanese Yen
d) 250 Japanese Yen in £
e) 700 Japanese Yen in £
f) 820 Japanese Yen in £.

Q24   The scale on a map is 1:10,000. How big are the following in real life:
a) a distance of 2 cm on the map
b) a distance of 20 cm on the map
c) a distance of 70 cm on the map
d) an area of 2 cm² on the map?

Maps are tricky, 'cos you've got to think about units. It's best to do the conversion in the units you're given, then do another conversion to appropriate units.

Q25   Another map has a scale of 1:3,000. What size on this map are the following:
a) a distance of 5 km in real life
b) a distance of 1 km in real life
c) an area of 100 m² in real life
d) an area of 50 m² in real life?

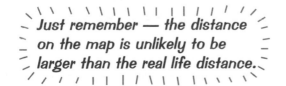

Just remember — the distance on the map is unlikely to be larger than the real life distance.

1.9   *Questions on Rounding Off*

Rounding a number off to a certain number of decimal places or significant figures is really quite easy — the tricky bit's when they ask for minimum and maximum values...

Q1   K = 456.9873
Write K correct to:

    a) one decimal place   **d)** three significant figures
    b) two decimal places   **e)** two significant figures
    c) three decimal places   **f)** one significant figure.

Q2   John divides £14.30 by 3. What is the answer correct to the nearest penny?

Q3   A rectangular rug is 1.8 metres long and 0.7 metres wide. Both measurements are given correct to one decimal place.

    a) State the minimum possible length of the rug.
    b) Calculate the maximum possible area of the rug.

Q4   Calculate, giving your answers to a sensible degree of accuracy:

    a) $\dfrac{42.65 \times 0.9863}{24.6 \times 2.43}$

    b) $\dfrac{13.63 + 7.22}{13.63 - 7.22}$

Remember — the real value could be anything up to half a unit above or below the rounded off value.

Q5   Sandra has a parcel to post. To find out how much it will cost she weighs it.
    a) A set of kitchen scales, that weigh to the nearest 10 g, show that the parcel weighs 90 g. Write down the largest weight that the parcel could be.
    b) Next she weighs the parcel on a different set of kitchen scales, which are accurate to the nearest 5 g. The packet weighs 95 g. Write down the upper and lower bounds of the weight of the package according to these scales.
    c) The post office weighs the parcel on some electronic scales to the nearest gram. It weighs 98 g. Can all the scales be right?

Q6 $R = \dfrac{S}{T}$ is a formula used by stockbrokers.

     S = 940, correct to 2 significant figures and T = 5.56, correct to 3 significant figures.

    a) For the value of S, write down the upper bound and the lower bound.
    b) For the value of T, write down the upper bound and the lower bound.
    c) Calculate the upper bound and lower bound for R.
    d) Write down the value of R correct to an appropriate number of significant figures.

Q7   Vince ran a 100 m race in 10.3 seconds. If the time was measured to the nearest 0.1 seconds and the distance to the nearest metre, what is the maximum value of his average speed, in metres per second?

1.9   Questions on Rounding Off

The trick to find the maximum/minimum of a calculation is to work out the <u>max/min</u> *values of* <u>each bit</u>, *then* <u>use both</u> *in the calculation.*

Q8 **a)** The length of a rectangle is measured as 12 ± 0.1 cm. The width of the same rectangle is measured as 4 ± 0.1 cm. Calculate the perimeter of the rectangle, giving also the maximum possible error.

  b) A rectangle measures $A \pm x$ cm in length and $B \pm y$ cm in width. The formula $P = 2(A + B)$ is used to calculate the perimeter, P, of the rectangle. What is the maximum possible error in P?

Q9 Thomas is using his new calculator. He presses ■8■ then ■√■. What is the answer correct to two decimal places?

Q10 Calculate, giving your answers to a sensible degree of accuracy:

  a) $\dfrac{18.95 \times 0.6464}{2.4 - 2.0}$

  b) $\dfrac{324 + 7.22}{243 - 7.2}$

Q11 Jodie weighs herself on some scales that are accurate to the nearest 10 grams. The digital display shows her weight as 64.78 kg.
  a) What is the maximum that she could weigh?
  b) What is the minimum that she could weigh?

Upper/Lower Bounds are just another way of saying the Maximum/Minimum possible values.

Q12 A = 13, correct to 2 significant figures.
   B = 12.5, correct to 3 significant figures.
  a) For the value of A, write down the upper bound and the lower bound.
  b) For the value of B, write down the upper bound and the lower bound.
  c) Calculate the upper bound and lower bound for C when C = AB.

Q13 A lorry travelled 125 kilometres in 1 hour and 50 minutes. If the time was measured to the nearest 10 minutes and the distance to the nearest five kilometres, what was the maximum value of the average speed of the lorry, in kilometres per hour?

Remember — you don't always get the maximum value by using the biggest input value.

Q14 Jimmy, Sarah and Douglas are comparing their best times for running the 1500 m.
   Jimmy's best time is 5 minutes 30 seconds measured to the nearest 10 seconds.
   Sarah's best time is also 5 minutes 30 seconds, but measured to the nearest 5 seconds.
   Douglas' best time is 5 minutes 26 seconds measured to the nearest second.

  a) What are the upper and lower bounds for Sarah's best time?
  b) Of the three Douglas thinks that he is the quickest at running the 1500 m. Explain why this may not be the case.

1.10   *Questions on Estimating*

Q1   Without using your calculator find approximate answers to the following:

a) 6560×1.97

b) 8091×1.456

c) $38.45 \times 1.4237 \times 5.0002$

d) $45.34 \div 9.345$

e) $34504 \div 7133$

f) $\dfrac{55.33 \times 19.345}{9.23}$

g) 7139×2.13

h) $98 \times 2.54 \times 2.033$

i) $21 \times 21 \times 21$

j) $8143 \div 81$

k) $62000 \div 950$

l) $\pi \div 3$

Q2   Estimate the area under the graph.

Always give your answer to one less significant figure than the question.

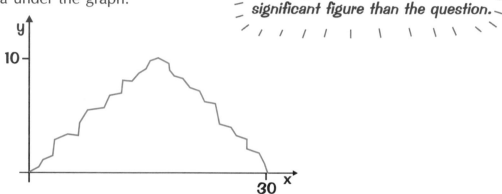

Q3   A supermarket chain sold 14634 tins of beans during a four week period.

a) If the supermarkets were open every day of the week, how many days did it take to sell the 14634 tins of beans?

b) What was the average amount of beans sold each day?

c) Show your working for a rough estimate to **b)** to check that your answer is of the right order of magnitude.

"of the right order of magnitude" is just a posh way to say "the right size", by the way.

Q4 π is the number of times that the diameter of a circle divides into the circumference. Many values have been used as estimates — here are a few examples:

$$3, \quad \frac{21}{7}, \quad \sqrt{10}, \quad \frac{255}{81}, \quad 3\tfrac{17}{120}.$$

a) Use your calculator to give each estimate correct to 7 decimal places.

b) Which is the most accurate estimate for π?

Q5   Showing all your working, estimate the value of the following:

a) $\dfrac{144.5 + 49.1}{153.2 - 41.2}$

b) $\dfrac{18.2 \times 10.7}{\sqrt{398.6}}$

c) $\dfrac{2021.23 \times 4.0436}{20.33 \times 4.902}$

d) $\dfrac{(9.2)^2 \div 10.3}{4.306 \times 5.011}$

If you don't show your working you'll lose easy marks so it's gotta be worth doing.

1.10   *Questions on Estimating*

Q6   A small swimming pool is approximately a cuboid in shape. The depth of the pool is 0.5m, the width is 5m and the length is 9m. Calculate the volume of the swimming pool in m^3 to

     a) 1dp   **b)** 1sf.

     c) State which of parts **a)** and **b)** would make the more reasonable value to use.

Q7   Round each of the following to an appropriate degree of accuracy:

     a) 41.798 g of flour used to make a bread loaf.

     b) A 28.274 cm length of wood used to make a shelf.

     c) 4.632 g of $C_{12}H_{22}O_{11}$ (sugar) for a scientific experiment.

     d) 2.159 litres of orange juice used in a fruit punch.

     e) 0.629 miles from Colin's house to the nearest shop.

     f) 32.382 miles per gallon.   *Just think — <u>casual</u>, <u>technical</u> or <u>really scientific</u>...*

Q8   Estimate the areas of the following:

     a) 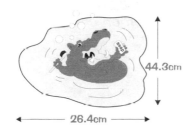   **b)**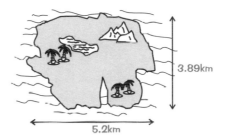

<u>Remember</u>, nice easy convenient numbers... <u>then</u> do the working out.

Q9   Estimate these volumes:

     a) 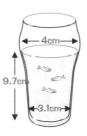   **b)**

Q10   Estimate the following square roots, to 1 dp:

     a) $\sqrt{48}$ **b)** $\sqrt{118}$ **c)** $\sqrt{84}$

     d) $\sqrt{17}$ **e)** $\sqrt{98}$ **f)** $\sqrt{34}$

<u>Start</u> with square roots that <u>you know</u> — and use them to make an educated <u>guess</u>.

Q11   Now estimate these (they're a bit harder) — again, to 1 dp:

     a) $\sqrt{41}$ **b)** $\sqrt{200}$ **c)** $\sqrt{30}$

     d) $\sqrt{150}$ **e)** $\sqrt{180}$ **f)** $\sqrt{140}$

Q12   Here is a sequence of square numbers. Use it to estimate (to 1 dp) the square roots below.

12	13	14	15	16	17	18	19	20
144	169	196	225	256	289	324	361	400

     a) $\sqrt{405}$ **b)** $\sqrt{270}$ **c)** $\sqrt{250}$ **d)** $\sqrt{375}$ **e)** $\sqrt{391}$

1.11 *Questions on Sequences*

Q1   10, 20, 15, 17½, 16¼...
a) Write down the next 4 terms.
b) Explain how you would work out the 10th term.
c) What is the limit of the sequence?

Q2   The first 3 terms of a sequence are: 1×2, $\sqrt{2} \times 3$, $\sqrt{3} \times 4$
a) Write down the next 3 terms.
b) Write down the nth term in its simplest form.

Q3   Write down the nth term:
a) 1, 4, 9, 16, 25...
b) 3, 6, 11, 18, 27...
c) 1, 8, 27, 64, 125...
d) ½, 4, 13½, 32, 62½...

Q4   Calculate the 100th term:
a) 1, 4, 9, 16 ...
b) 1, $\sqrt{2}$, $\sqrt{3}$, $\sqrt{4}$ ...
c) $\sqrt{3}$, 2, $\sqrt{5}$, $\sqrt{6}$ ...
d) $\sqrt{2}$, $\sqrt{4}$, $\sqrt{6}$, $\sqrt{8}$, $\sqrt{10}$ ...

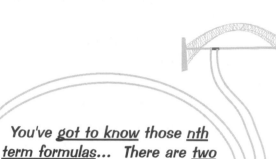

You've <u>got to know</u> those <u>nth</u> term formulas... There are <u>two</u> of the things to go at, and they're <u>bound</u> to give you a question on one of them.

Q5   The nth term of a sequence is n(n + 1).
a) Write down the first 3 terms (n = 1,2,3).
b) Explain why every term in the sequence is even.
c) Write down the nth term of another sequence in which every term is even.
d) Write down the nth term of a sequence in which every term is odd.

Q6   Jimmy uses some stones to make a pattern.
a) How many stones will there be in the next block?
b) How many stones will there be in the nth block?
c) There are 2600 stones in a block. Use your answer to **b)** to find the corresponding value for n.

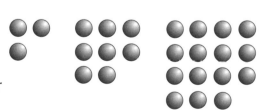

Q7   Sequence A   1, 4, 9, 16, 25,...
Sequence B   3, 6, 9, 12, 15,...
Sequence C   2, 5, 9, 14, 20,...

a) Write down the next three terms in sequence A.
b) Write down the next three terms in sequence B.
c) Write down the nth term of sequence A.
d) Write down the nth term of sequence B.
e) Sequence C is obtained from sequences A and B. Using this information and your answers to parts **c)** and **d)** work out the nth term for sequence C.
f) Calculate the 80th term of sequence C.

1.11   *Questions on Sequences*

Q8 $1, -\dfrac{1}{2}, \dfrac{1}{4}, -\dfrac{1}{8} \ldots$ *If the difference between terms is always decreasing, there's going to be a limit to the sequence.*

    a) Write down the next 3 terms.
    b) What is the nth term of the sequence?
    c) What is the limit of the sequence?

You won't get many of these, and anyway it's obvious when it happens (like in Q8) so don't worry too much.

Q9   The first 3 terms of a sequence are $(2 \times 3)^2$, $(3 \times 4)^2$, $(4 \times 5)^2$.
    a) Write down the next 3 terms.
    b) Write down the nth term.

Q10   Calculate the 34th term in the following sequences:

    a) $1, \dfrac{1}{2}, \dfrac{1}{3}, \dfrac{1}{4} \ldots$ **c)** 0, 3, 8, 15, 24...

    b) 10, 20, 30, 40...   **d)** $1, x, x^2, x^3, x^4 \ldots$

Q11   The first term of a certain sequence is 1. The second term of the sequence is also 1. The nth term is found using the following formula:
       nth term = (n —1)th term + (n — 2)th term.
    Calculate the third, fourth, and fifth terms in the sequence.

Q12   The first four terms of a sequence are x, 4x, 9x, 16x.
    a) For x = 2 write down the next two terms in the sequence.
    b) For x = 2 write down the nth term in the sequence.
    c) For x = 3 write down the nth term in the sequence.
    d) Write down the nth term, valid for any value of x.
    e) For x = ½ calculate the 75th term in the sequence.

Q13   Each term in a sequence is the mean of the previous three terms.
    a) If the first three terms are 1, 2, 3, what are the next three terms in the sequence?
    b) If the first three terms are x+1, x+2, x+3, what are the next three terms in the sequence?
    c) If the first three terms are ½, ½, ½, what is the nth term?
    d) If the first three terms are x, x, x, what is the nth term?

Q14   The first five terms of a sequence are x+1, x+2, x+3, x+4, x+5.
    a) For x=10 write down the next term in the sequence.
    b) For x=10 write down the nth term in the sequence.
    c) For x=100 write down the nth term in the sequence.
    d) For x=n write down the nth term in the sequence.
    e) Write down the nth term, valid for any value of x.
    f) For x=−400 calculate the 400th term in the sequence.

1.11 Questions on Sequences

Q15 What are these sequences called and what are their next 3 terms and nth terms?
a) 2, 4, 6, 8, ...
b) 1, 3, 5, 7, ...
c) 1, 4, 9, 16, ...
d) 1, 8, 27, 64, ...
e) 1, 3, 6, 10, ...

Just give each picture a number, then do these the same as before

Q16 Using pencils, Graham made a pattern:

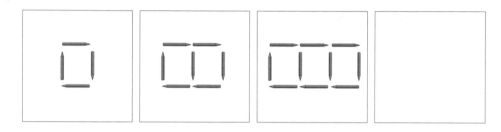

a) Write down the number of pencils in each group.
b) How many pencils would be in the next group along?
c) Find a formula for the number of pencils in the nth group.

Q17

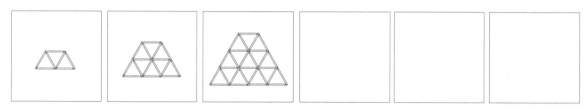

The pattern above is based on individual triangles.
a) Write down the number of triangles in each group.
b) Work out the number of triangles that would be in each of the next three groups.
c) Find a formula for the number of triangles in the nth term of the pattern.

Q18 A square tile pattern is formed with grey and white tiles. In the centre there is always a grey tile. The rest of the pattern is made up of grey and white tiles, with the four corner tiles of the square always being grey.
The first term of the pattern is shown.

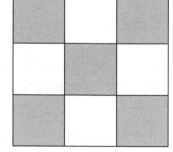

Work out the formula for:
a) the number of grey tiles
b) the number of white tiles
c) the total number of tiles.

Q19 In the following sequences, write down the next 3 terms and the nth term:
a) 7, 10, 13, 16,...   c) 6, 16, 26, 36,...
b) 12, 17, 22, 27,...   d) 54, 61, 68, 75,...

1.11 Questions on Sequences

Q20 Baz is collecting the post for his grandfather while he is away on holiday. On the first day he was away he received 3 letters. On the second day the pile of letters had grown to 6. By the third day, Baz had 9 letters in all.
This pattern continued while his grandfather was away, and he returned from his holiday on the ninth day.
a) How many letters were waiting for him?
b) How many letters would have been waiting if he had returned on the nth day?

Q21 Write down the next three terms and nth term of:
a) 5, 8, 12, 17,...
c) 9, 12, 19, 30,...
b) 6, 9, 14, 21,...
d) 14, 19, 27, 38,...

Q22 For each of the following sequences, write down the next three terms:
a) 1, 4, 16, 64,...
c) 6, 12, 24, 48,...
b) 3, 15, 75, 375,...
d) 9, 27, 81, 243,...

Q23 Nobby collects novelty boots. In order to increase his collection he placed an advert in a national newspaper asking members of the public to send him novelty boots. On first day he received 2 boots. The second day he had received 6 boots in total. By the end of third day he had received 18 boots in total. How many boots had Nobby received by the end of the:

a) 4th day
b) 6th day
c) 10th day
d) nth day.

With questions like these, it doesn't actually tell you that the pattern continues — but since it's the sequences section, you're fairly safe in assuming it.

Q24 For each of the following sequences, write down the next three terms:

a) 729, 243, 81, 27,...
b) 31250, 6250, 1250, 250,...
c) 12288, 3027, 768, 192,...
d) 5103, 1701, 567, 189,...

Q25 In order to work out the evaporation rate, Joanna measured the area of a puddle of water every hour on the hour. At 1300h the area of the puddle was 128 cm². 1 hour later the area of the puddle was 64 cm². At 1500h the area was 32 cm².

a) What was the area of the puddle of water at 1600h?
b) What was the area of the puddle at 1800h?

2.1   Questions on Regular Polygons

The one thing they're <u>guaranteed</u> to ask you about is <u>Interior and</u> <u>Exterior Angles</u> — you'd better get learning those formulas...

Q1   ABCDEFGH is a regular octagon.
Calculate the size of the angle BCD.

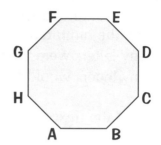

Q2

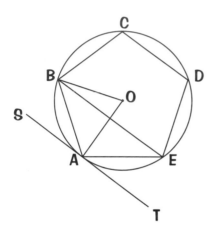

ABCDE is a regular pentagon. It is drawn in a circle centre O. SAT is a tangent drawn to the circle at A.

a) Calculate the size of angle BOA.
b) Find the size of angle OBA.
c) Write down the size of angle:
  i) SAO
  ii) BAS.
d) Hence write down the size of angle BEA giving a reason for your answer.

Q3   What is the angle between two adjacent sides of a 12 sided regular polygon?

Q4   The sum of the interior angles of a regular polygon is 2520°. How many sides has this regular polygon?

Q5 **a)** Describe fully the transformation that would map triangle ABO onto triangle DEO so that A mapped onto D, B onto E and O remained unchanged.

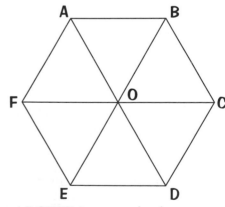

ABCDEF is a regular hexagon.

  b) Describe fully the transformation that would map triangle ABO onto triangle CDO so that A mapped onto C, B onto D and O remained unchanged.
  c) Describe fully the transformation that would map triangle ABO onto triangle EDO so that A mapped onto E, B onto D and O remained unchanged.
  d) Describe fully the transformation that would map triangle BOC onto triangle AFO so that B mapped onto A, C mapped onto F and O remained unchanged.
  e) Describe fully the transformation that would map triangle ABO onto triangle AOF so that A and O remained unchanged and B mapped onto F.
  f) Describe fully the transformation that would map triangle ABO onto triangle BOC so that A mapped onto B, B mapped onto C and O remained unchanged.

2.1   Questions on Regular Polygons

Q6 ABCDEFG is a regular heptagon with centre O.

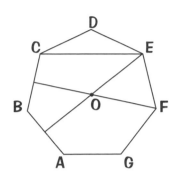

a) Make a copy of the figure and mark on it the axis of symmetry which maps E onto F.

b) Hence give a reason why triangle OEF is isosceles.

c) Find the size of angles CDE and DCE, correct to 1 decimal place.

d) Give a reason why CE is parallel to AG.

Q7

The figure shows part of a regular polygon.

a) Write down the value of the angle X.

b) Hence calculate how many sides the polygon has.

Q8 The figure shows part of a regular 9 sided figure. Its centre is O. Calculate the size of angles:

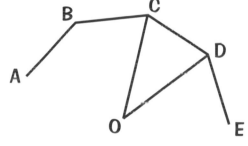

a) COD

b) OCD

c) ABC.

Q9 ABCDE is a regular pentagon whose vertices lie on a circle of radius 5 cm, centre O. DOM is an axis of symmetry of the pentagon and cuts the chord AB at X.

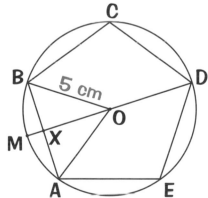

a) Calculate the size of angle BOX.

b) Find the length OX. Hence find the distance of M from the chord AB.

c) Find also the length of the arc AM.

Q10 Jim argued that is was possible to construct a regular polygon in which each exterior angle is 28°. James said it was not. Who is right?

Q11 A polygon has an interior angle of 168°. Can this polygon be regular? If so, state how many sides it has.

Q12 ABCDEFGH is a regular octagon.

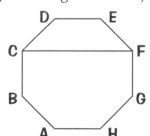

a) Copy the figure and mark on the axis of symmetry which maps H to A.

b) Calculate the size of angle EFC.

2.2 Questions on Areas

For perimeters, the __Big Blob Method__ is the __best way__ to be sure you've got all the sides.

Q1 The diagram shows a plan of Julian's garden.
a) Calculate the perimeter of the garden.
b) Find the area of the garden.

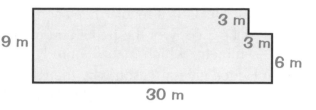

Julian wishes to buy turf to cover the complete area of the garden. Turf is sold in units of 4 m².

c) Work out how many units Julian needs to cover the whole garden.
d) Turf costs £7.90 per unit plus £12.50 for delivery. Find the total cost of the turf plus delivery.

Q2 A 45 m length of cooking foil is 45 cm wide. Find the area of foil on the roll in m².

Q3 The diagram shows a trapezium ABCD in which DC is parallel to AB.

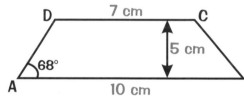

a) Angle BAD = 68°. Find the size of angle ADC.
b) AB = 10 cm. CD = 7 cm. The perpendicular distance between the parallel sides is 5 cm. Calculate the area of the trapezium.

Q4 ABCDE is a pentagon as shown.
a) Length BC = 1.8 m and angle CBG = 20°. Calculate the length of BG.
b) Length AB = 5 m and length AH = 0.8 m. Calculate the length of BH.
c) Find the height CF of the pentagon.
d) Given that the pentagon is symmetrical about its height calculate:
   i) the width AE of the pentagon
   ii) the area of the pentagon ABCDE.

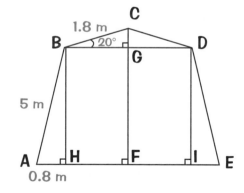

Work out the individual areas first, then add them together or take bits off to make the area you need. If only everything in life was this simple...

Q5 Lengths are denoted by a, b and h. Which formulas represent areas?
a) $\pi(a + b)$
b) $\pi h(a + b)^2$
c) $\pi^2 h$
d) $\pi(a + b)h$
e) $\pi(a + b)h^2$

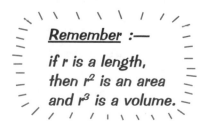

__Remember :—__ if r is a length, then r^2 is an area and r^3 is a volume.

2.2   *Questions on Areas*

Q6   An open box has dimensions as shown.

    a) Write down an expression in terms of x for the total surface area of the open box (A). Simplify this expression as far as possible.

    b) Complete the table below for values of x and A.

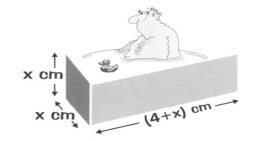

x cm

x cm   (4+x) cm

x	2	4	6	8	10	12	14	16
A		128			620			

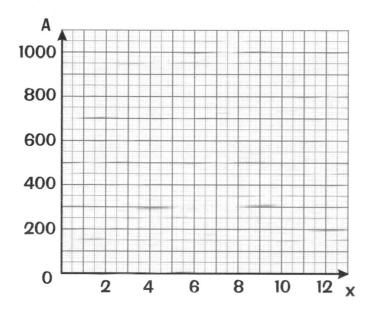

    c) Draw the graph of A against x.

    d) Write down from your graph the value of x which gives an area of 300 cm².

Q7   A playground is to contain a sand pit. It is in the shape of a cylinder of diameter 5 m and height 0.8 m. It must be lined on the bottom and on the walls with plastic sheet. Find:

    a) the area of the sand pit which must be lined

    b) the number of sheets required if each sheet is sold in the form of rectangles 1.3 m long and 0.5 m wide.

    The mass of 1 m³ of sand is 1.4 tonnes. Find:

    c) the volume of sand required in m³

    d) the mass of sand required to the nearest tonne.

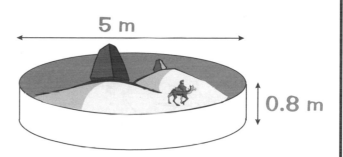

5 m

0.8 m

2.2   Questions on Areas

Remember what I said about these tricky area questions —
you'll find them quite easy if you split them into simple shapes.

Q8   A plastic strip is made in the shape shown. The curves AC and BD are both arcs of circles with centre O. The larger circle has radius 30 mm and the smaller circle has radius 20 mm. The shaded ends of the shape are both semicircles.

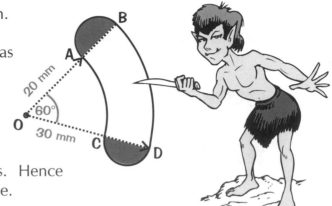

a) Find the area of the shape ABDC.

b) Find the area of the two semicircular ends. Hence write down the area of the complete shape.

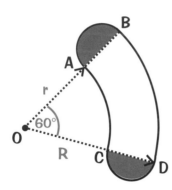

Suppose the radius of the arc AC is now r and that of BD is R.

c) Write down a formula for the area of the sector OBD in terms of R.

d) Write down an expression for the area of the shape ABDC in terms of r and R.

e) Hence write down an expression for the area of the complete shape.

Q9   ABCD is a field with AB = 100 m, BC = 90 m and CD = 60 m. DE is a fence across the field with EA = x m.

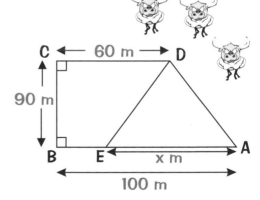

a) Find the area of the field ABCD.

b) Find an expression in terms of x for the area of triangle DEA.

c) The fence DE is arranged so that the ratio of the area of triangle DEA : area of trapezium BEDC = 3:5.

    i) Find the value of x for this ratio.

    ii) Write down the area of triangle DEA using the value of x found in **i)**.

Q10

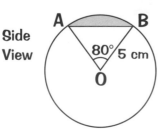

Side View

A washing powder ball looks from the side like a circle with the shaded area removed. The circle has radius 5 cm and the angle AOB = 80°.

a) Find the area of the sector OAB.

b) Find the area of triangle AOB and hence the area of the shaded area.

2.3   *Questions on Volumes*

Make sure you know the <u>4 main volume formulas</u> — <u>spheres</u>, <u>prisms</u>, <u>pyramids</u>, <u>cones</u>.

Q1   a, b and h are lengths. Which of the following formulas could represent a volume? Give a reason for your answer.

   a) πabh **c)** $\pi h^2(a + b)$

   b) $\pi(a + b)h$ **d)** $\pi h^2(a + b)^2$

Q2   Joe buys a garden cloche to protect his plants from frost. It has a semicircular diameter of 70 cm and a length of 3 m.

   a) Find the cross sectional area.

   b) Hence find the volume of the cloche.

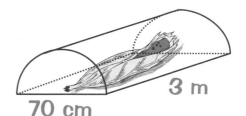

3 m

70 cm

Q3   In my garden I have a circular pond which is surrounded by a ring shaped paved area. The pond is 35 cm deep. The pond is filled with water.

   a) Find the volume of water in the pond when full.

   b) Find the area of paving surrounding the pond.

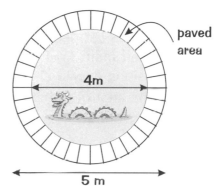

paved area

4m

5 m

Q4

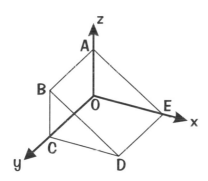

The diagram shows a triangular prism.
The coordinates of A are (0, 0, 5).
The coordinates of E are (4, 0, 0).
The coordinates of C are (0, 8, 0).

   a) Write down the coordinates of:

      i) B

      ii) D.

   b) Calculate the volume of the prism.

Q5   A cuboid has a height of x m, a width of (3–x) m and a length of (5-x) m.

   a) Write down an expression for the volume of the cuboid.

   b) Complete the table of values using your expression for the volume of the cuboid.

x	0	1	2	3
V			6	

   c) Draw a graph of V against x for $0 \leqslant x \leqslant 3$.

   d) Use your graph to find the maximum volume of the cuboid.

   e) Find the surface area of the cuboid when the volume is at its maximum.

   f) A particular cuboid has a volume of 6 m³. By using your graph to find the two possible values of x, find the maximum total surface area of the cuboid for this volume.

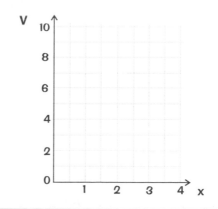

2.3 *Questions on Volumes*

Q6 Bill bought a new garden shed with dimensions as shown. Find:

a) the area of the cross section

b) the volume of the shed

c) the length AB

d) the total area of the roof.

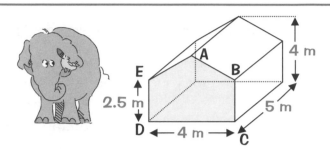

Q7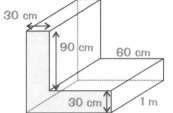

Jill buys a bookshelf with the dimensions shown in the diagram.

a) Find the cross sectional area.

b) Find the volume of the bookshelf in m³.

Q8 Busy Buses Ltd decide to put a bus shelter near their main town centre stop. It has the dimensions shown.

a) Find the area of the cross section of the shelter.

b) Find its volume.

Contrary to popular belief, there isn't anything that complicated about prisms — they're only solids with the same shape all the way through. The only bit that sometimes takes a little longer is finding the cross-sectional area.

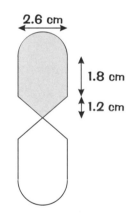

Q9 An egg timer is symmetrical and consists of hemispheres, cylinders and cones joined together as shown.

a) Calculate the volume of sand in the upper container. Sand runs into the bottom container at a constant rate of 0.05 cm³ per second.

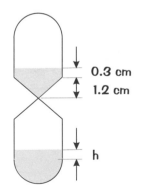

At the end of a certain time period the sand has fallen through into the bottom container as shown.

b) How high (**h**) has it risen up the cylindrical part of the bottom container?

c) How long has it taken the sand to fall through until it is at this height?

Q10 A metal cube, each of whose sides is 10 cm long, is melted down and made into a cylinder 10 cm high. What is the radius of this cylinder?

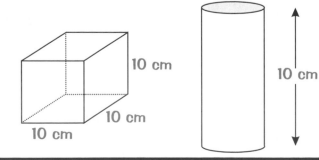

2.3 *Questions on Volumes*

Don't get confused when they've only given you the volumes of liquids — you still use the same volume equations, but you've got to rearrange them a bit. Go on, give it a go.

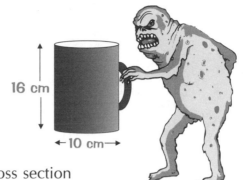

Q11 A tin mug has the dimensions shown.
  a) What is the greatest volume of milk the mug can hold?
  b) In fact, 600 cm³ of milk is poured in. How high will it go up the mug?

16 cm

←10 cm→

Q12

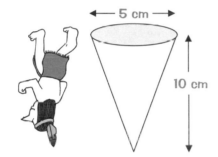

3 cm

3 cm   5 mm

A nut has the cross section illustrated. The circular hole has a diameter of 1.4 cm and the nut is 5 mm thick.
Find the volume of the nut in cm³.

(Units...)

Q13

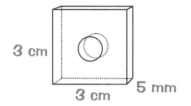

←— 5 cm —→

10 cm

A biscuit cone is 10 cm deep and has a base diameter of 5 cm. It is completely filled with ice cream and a hemisphere of ice cream is mounted on top so that the base of the hemisphere coincides with the base of the cone.

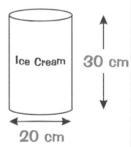

Ice Cream   30 cm

20 cm

  a) Calculate the volume of ice cream required to make one ice cream.
  b) How many ice creams can be made from a cylinder 20 cm in diameter and 30 cm high, which is three quarters full of ice cream?

Q14

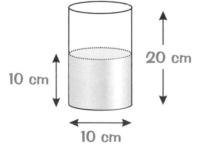

20 cm

10 cm

10 cm

A cylindrical container of diameter 10 cm and height 20 cm is filled with water to a depth of 10 cm. 3,200 identical ball bearings are now submerged in the water. The depth increases to 18 cm. Calculate the radius of one ball bearing.

Q15 Water is flowing into each of these containers at a constant rate. For each container, sketch the graph of the depth of water against time.

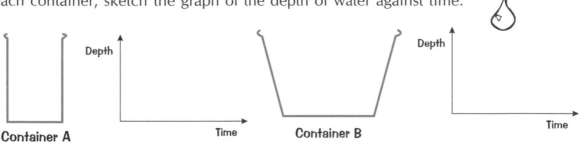

Depth

Container A   Time   Container B

Depth

Time

2.4 Questions on Nets and Scale Drawings

There are 4 nets that you need to know inside out... so to speak:
1) Triangular Prism, 2) Cube, 3) Cuboid, 4) Pyramid. But don't go thinking you can stop
there... they could spring anything on you in the exam if they like...

Q1

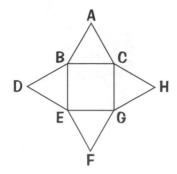

The diagram shows the net of a solid in which ABC is an equilateral triangle, BCGE is a square.

a) Which points will coincide with A when the net is folded up to make the solid?

b) Describe the symmetry of the net.

c) How many faces, edges and vertices does it have when in solid form?

Q2   A pyramid has a square base of side 3 units. Its height AB is 1 unit and A is the mid point of the square.

a) State the coordinates of B.

b) Calculate the angle between the edge OB and OA.

c) Sketch a net for the pyramid.

When you're drawing a net, think of making the thing out of cardboard.

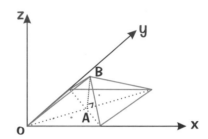

Q3   The diagram shows the net of a cube of edge 8 cm.

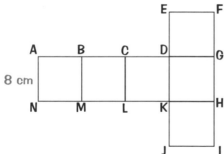

a) Which point coincides with M when the net is folded to make the cube?

b) Find the area of the face DGHK.

c) What is the total surface area of the cube?

d) Draw a 3-D scale drawing of the completed cube.

Q4   The diagram shows the net of a solid. EFGH is a square which forms the base. Triangles ABC, BCD, CDE and CFE are equilateral triangles. Length GH = 6 cm.

a) What shape is the solid when assembled?

b) Which point coincides with B when the net is assembled to make the solid?

c) If X is the mid point of FE, show that CX is 5.20 cm.

d) Find the total surface area of the solid.

e) Find the height of the solid.

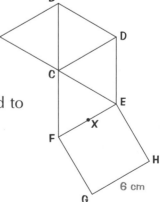

Q5

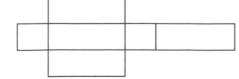

This diagram shows a net for a rectangular box with a lid. For the same box sketch a different net.

2.4 Questions on Nets and Scale Drawings

Q6 Which of these two nets will form a pyramid on a triangular base with all four faces equilateral triangles?

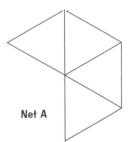

Net A

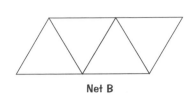

Net B

Q7 A net is cut out from a cardboard rectangle as shown in the diagram.

a) Show that the net forms a box with no lid by drawing the solid, adding on all measurements in terms of x.

b) Write down an expression for the volume V of the box in terms of x.

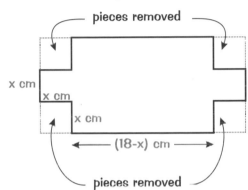

pieces removed

x cm

x cm

x cm

(18-x) cm

pieces removed

c) Fill in the values of V in this table.

x	8	10	12	14	16
V		800			

d) Draw the graph of V against x.

e) Write down from your graph the value of x which makes the volume a maximum. Hence also write down this maximum volume.

f) Calculate the surface area when the volume takes its maximum value.

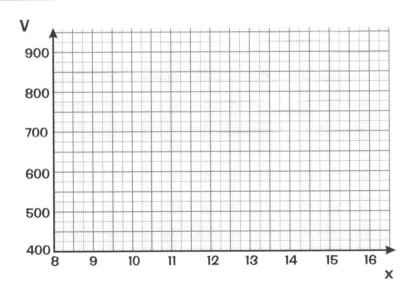

Q8 The diagram shows an isometric projection of a triangular prism.

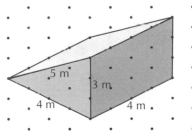

5 m

3 m

4 m   4 m

Draw:
a) the front elevation
b) the side elevation
c) the plan.

SECTION TWO — SHAPES

2.5 Questions on Loci and Constructions

Don't let a silly word like <u>locus</u> put you off — there are <u>easy marks</u> to be had here, but you've got to do everything neatly, using a pencil, ruler and compasses.

Q1 Inside the rectangle:
a) draw the locus of points 5 cm from D
b) draw the locus of points equidistant from A and D
c) indicate by an X, the point inside the rectangle which is 5 cm from D and equidistant from A and D.

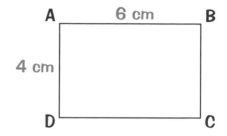

Q2 Construct triangle PQR accurately with Length PQ = 10.5 cm, angle PQR = 95° and angle RPG = 32°.

a) Draw in the perpendicular bisector of the line PR. Draw in point A where the bisector crosses the line PQ.
b) Bisect angle PRQ. Draw in point B where the bisector crosses the line PQ. Measure the length BA.

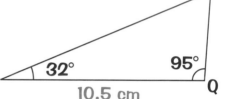

Q3 To win a bet, a man had to walk round his house remaining exactly 3 m from it all the way round.

Using a scale of 1 m to 1 cm draw the locus of the man's movement round the house, marking the walls of the house clearly on your diagram.

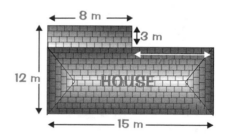

Q4 A and B are 2 points on a straight shore, 4 km apart with A due West of B.
a) Describe the locus of points P such that angle APB equals 90°.
b) Using a scale of 2 cm to 1 km draw an accurate scale diagram showing A, B, the shore line and the locus of P.
An outcrop of rock is located on a bearing of 060° from A and 300° from B.
c) Indicate the rock on your diagram. Mark the spot with an X.
d) A ship steaming due East parallel to the shore avoids the rock by following the locus of P. How near does the ship come to the rock?

Q5 Construct triangle PQR with length PQ = QR = 11.5 cm and angle PQR = 38°.
a) Draw the bisectors of angles QPR and QRP. Mark the point O where the 2 bisectors cross.
b) With centre O draw the circle which just touches the sides PQ, PR and QR of the triangle. What is the radius of this circle?.

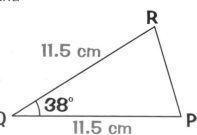

2.5   Questions on Loci and Constructions

Q6   This is a plan of Simon's room. To keep warm Simon must be within 2 m of the wall containing the radiator. To see out of the window he must be within 1.5 m of the wall containing the window.

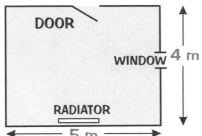

a) Using a scale of 2 cm to 1 m draw a plan of Simon's room.

b) Shade the region in which Simon must be if he is to be warm and see out of the window.

Q7   A running track is designed so that each point on the track is 32.5 m from a fixed line AB which is 100 m long.

a) Draw the locus of the line.

b) Calculate the distance once round the running track.

Q8   The diagram shows a plan of Jim's back garden. Two sides of the garden are bounded by fences and the other sides are bounded by the walls of the house and garage. The garden is in the form of a rectangle.

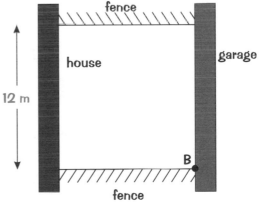

a) Using a scale of 1 cm to 1 m draw a plan of Jim's garden.

b) Ben, the friendly rotweiller, is tethered to the garage at B by a chain of length 3 m. Construct accurately and shade the part of the garden where Ben can go.

c) Jim wants to plant a tree in the garden. The tree must be planted more than 5 m away from the walls of the house and more than 4 m away from each fence. On the plan of the garden, construct accurately and shade the region where Jim can plant his tree.

Q9   The positions of two islands A and B are found from the following information:
A is 35 km from a jetty J on a bearing 065°, B is due south of A and on a bearing of 132° from J as shown below.

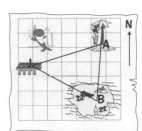

a) Using a scale of 1 cm to 5 km, draw an accurate plan to show the positions of J, A and B.

b) Find from your drawing the distance in km between the islands A and B.

c) A boat leaves the jetty at 09.00 and reaches A at 11.30. What is its average speed in km/h?

d) A lightship L is 20 km from J, equidistant from A and B and on the same side of J as A and B. Mark L on the drawing.

e) Find the bearing of J from L.

2.6   *Questions on Geometry*

Q1   In the diagram shown length GD = length GF
and line AC is parallel to line EG.
Write down the size of the following angles,
giving reasons for your answers:

a) angle DFG

b) angle EFH

c) angle DBC.

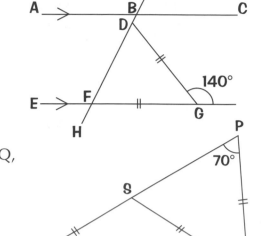

Q2   In the diagram length SR = length SQ = length PQ,
angle SQR = 35° and angle RPQ = 70°. Find:

a) angle PQS

b) angle RSQ

— giving reasons for your answers.

c) Explain why RSP is a straight line.

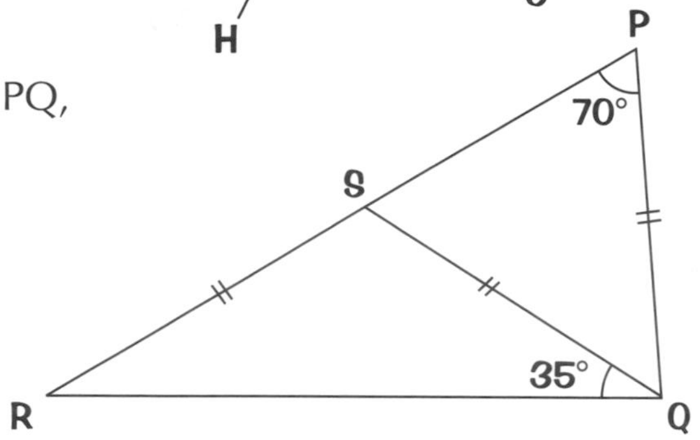

    *Angle Rules — there's an absolute stack of the darn things... and you can't
get away without knowing them, I'm afraid, so you'd better get learning.*

Q3

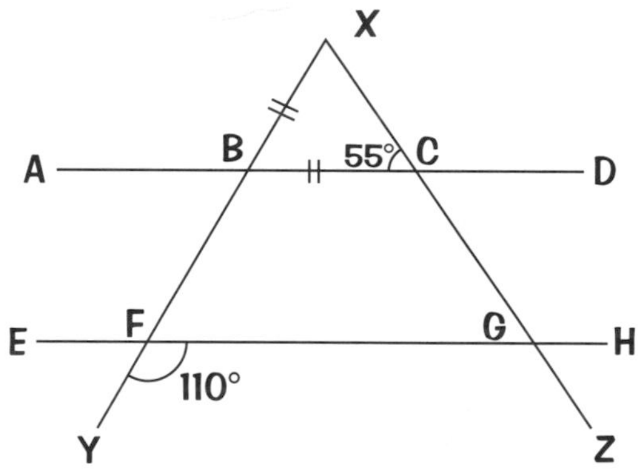

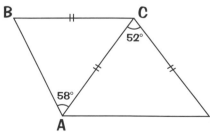

In the diagram length BX = length BC.

a) Calculate angle XBC giving a reason for
your answer.

b) Give a reason why AD is parallel to EH.

c) Write down the size of angle CGF.

Q4 a) Copy the figure and fill in all the
missing angles.

b) Explain why length EB = length EC.

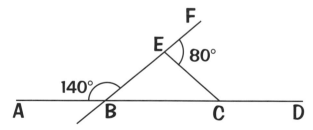

Q5   Lengths CB, CA and CD are equal, angle ACD = 52° and angle BAC = 58°

a) Write down the size of the following angles:

  i) BCA

  ii) CAD.

b) Give a reason why BC is parallel to AD.

c) Draw a line from B to D. Find angle CBD.

Q6 a) Write down the size of the following angles:

  i) AEB   **ii)** ECD   **iii)** ECB

b) Explain why:

  i) the line DA is parallel to the line CB

  ii) length EC = length ED

  iii) the line EB is not parallel to the line DC.

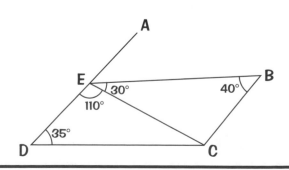

2.6   *Questions on Geometry*

Q7   Copy the figure and fill in the missing angles.

    a) Explain why the lengths

      i)   CA = AB

      ii)   CA = CD

      iii) CA = CE.

    b) Explain which line is parallel to BE.

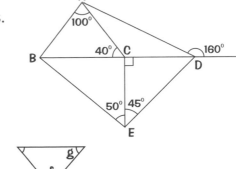

Q8   Find the angles marked a to g.

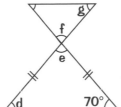

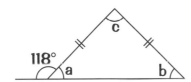

Q9   In the trapezium ABCD: length AB = length BC, angle ABC = 142°, angle DAC = 90° and the line AB is parallel to the line DC.

     Calculate, giving reasons
for your answers, angles:

    a) BAC

    b) ACD

    c) ADC.

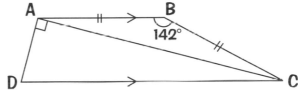

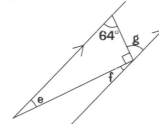

Keep an eye out for those tell-tale arrows — if you can spot they're parallel lines, you'll be well away. (As long as you can remember the rules for parallel lines , of course...)

Q10   Find all the angles marked from a to n.

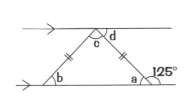

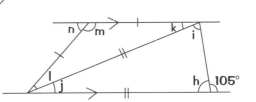

Q11   Length DA = length DC, length CA = length CB, the line DA is parallel to the line CE and angle FCG = 66°.

     Find, giving reasons for your answers, the angles:

    a) ACB

    b) DAC

    c) ABC

    d) ABE

    e) ADC.

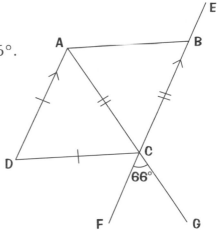

SECTION TWO — SHAPES

2.6 Questions on Geometry

Yet more dull pages — just lots of boring angles... still, that's geometry for you.
And it's really quite easy if you can <u>remember all those rules</u>...

Q12 Find the size of the angles marked from a to k.

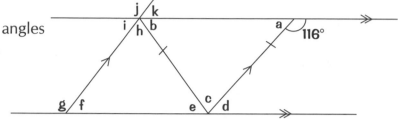

Q13 ABCD is a square and DEC is an equilateral triangle. Calculate with reasons, the following angles:

a) EDF

b) DFC

c) BFC.

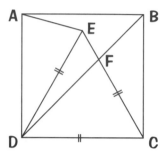

Q14

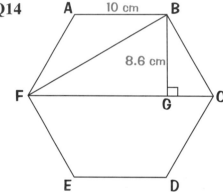

ABCDEF is a regular hexagon of side 10 cm.

a) Write down the sum of its interior angles.

b) Calculate the size of angle AFB.

c) Give a reason why the line FC is parallel to the line AB.

d) Length BG = 8.6 cm and the line FC is twice as long as the line AB.

   i) Calculate the length of CG.

   ii) Find the area of triangle BGC.

   iii) Calculate the area of the hexagon.

Q15 In ABCD, AB is parallel to DC and DB = BC, angle DBC = 70° and angle DAB = 55°.

a) Find angle BCD and angle ABD giving reasons for your answer.

b) Show that triangle DAB is isosceles.

c) Give a reason why AD is parallel to BC.

d) State the symmetries possessed by quadrilateral ABCD, and name which type of quadrilateral ABCD is.

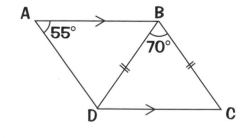

Q16 In the diagram the line AB is parallel to the line FC and the line AE is parallel to the line BD.
Angle BDC = 75° and angle ADE = 35°.

Write down the size of the following angles, stating reasons for your answer:

a) BCD

b) DBC

c) ADB

d) AEC

e) EAD

f) DAB.

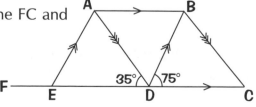

2.6   *Questions on Geometry*

Q17 ABCDE is a regular pentagon.

a) Calculate the size of angle BAE.

b) Deduce the size of angle:
  i) AEB
  ii) BED.

c) Make a copy of the figure and mark on it the axis of symmetry which maps D on to E.

d) Deduce the size of angle EBD.

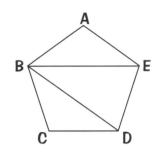

Don't forget — with geometry, the more you do it, the easier it gets... honestly.

Q18 Calculate the angles x, y and z in the diagram.

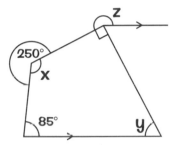

Q19 ABCD is a rhombus. The lines AC and BD are the axes of symmetry. Angle BDC = 40°. Calculate:

a) angle CBD

b) angle CBA

c) angle BCA.

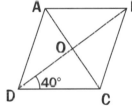

Q20 ABC is a triangle with the length BC equal to the length BD. Calculate, giving reasons:

a) angle DCB

b) angle ABC.

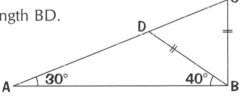

Q21

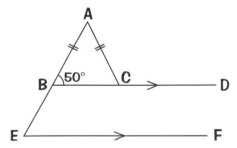

ABC is a triangle with the lengths AB and AC equal. The lines BD and EF are parallel, angle ABC = 50°. Write down the size of angles:

a) BEF

b) BAC

c) ACD.

Q22 ABCD is a kite. Lengths AX = 5 cm and BX = 3 cm. Calculate to the nearest degree:

a) Angle ABC

b) Angle BAC.

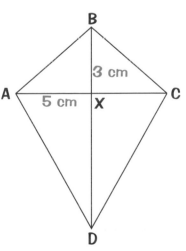

If BAD = 110° calculate:

c) angle CAD

d) the length of DX correct to 3 significant figures.

2.7 Questions on Circle Geometry

Just when you thought geometry was getting easy... now you've got circles to contend with. **Eeeek.**

Q1 ABCD is a cyclic quadrilateral with angle BCD = 100°.
EF is a tangent to the circle touching it at A.
Angle DAF = 30°.
Write down the size of angle:

a) BAD

b) EAB.

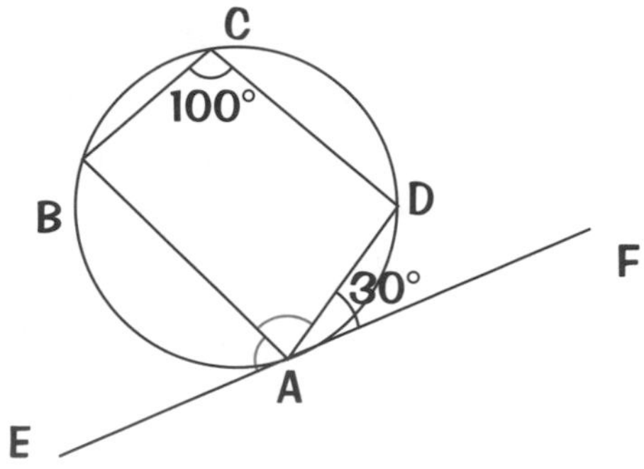

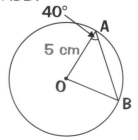

Q2

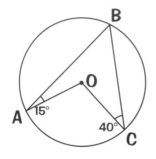

A, B and C are points on the circumference of a circle and O is the centre. Angle BAO = 15° and angle BCO = 40°. Find:

a) angle ABC

b) angle AOC.

Q3 A, B, C, D and E are points on the circumference of a circle centre O. Angle BDE = 53°. The line AF is a tangent to the circle, touching it at A. Angle EAF = 32°. Find:

a) angle BOE

b) angle ACE.

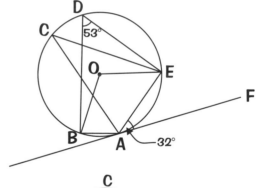

Q4 ABCD is a cyclic quadrilateral and the tangent to the circle at A makes an angle of 70° with the side AD. Angle BCA = 30°. Write down, giving a reason, the size of:

a) angle ACD

b) angle BAD.

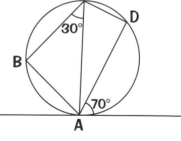

Q5

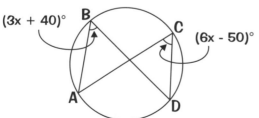

A, B, C and D are points on the circumference of a circle. Angle ABD = (3x + 40)° and angle ACD = (6x − 50)°.

a) Give a reason why angle ABD and angle ACD are the same.

b) Form an equation in x and by solving it, find the size of angle ABD.

Q6 A circle centre O has radius OA = 5cm.
Angle OAB = 40°. Calculate the length of the chord AB.

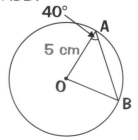

 Beware the sneaky isosceles...

2.7 Questions on Circle Geometry

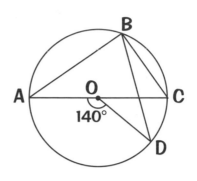

Q7 A, B, C and D are points on the circumference of a circle. O is the centre of the circle and angle AOD = 140°. Write down:
a) angle ABD
b) angle ABC
c) angle DBC.

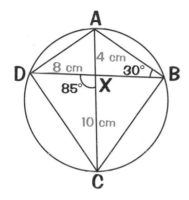

Q8 ABCD is a cyclic quadrilateral. The lines AC and BD intersect at X. Lengths AX = 4 cm, DX = 8 cm and XC = 10 cm. Angles DXC = 85° and ABD = 30°.
a) Show that triangles DXC and AXB are similar.
b) Find the length of XB.
c) Write down the size of angle BDC.

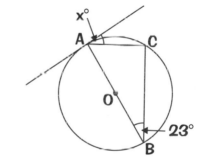

Q9 A tangent is drawn to a circle touching it at A. C and B are two other points on the circumference and AOB is a diameter. O is the centre of the circle. Angle ABC is 23°.
a) Write down the size of angle ACB, give a reason for your answer.
b) Find the size of the angle marked x° in the diagram.

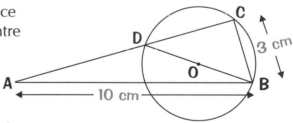

Q10 B, C and D are three points on the circumference of a circle with BD as a diameter. O is the centre of the circle and ADC is a straight line. AB = 10 cm and BC = 3 cm.
a) Write down the size of angle ACB, give a reason for your answer.
b) Show that AC is 9.54 cm correct to 2 decimal places.
c) If AD = 5 cm find the length of the diameter DOB correct to 2 decimal places.

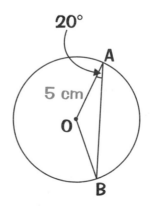

Q11 O is the centre of a circle and AB is a chord. The length OA = 5 cm and angle OAB = 20°. Find the length of the chord AB.

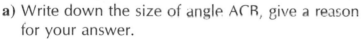
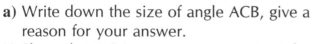

It's just a few simple chords, that's all...

2.8 Questions on Similarity and Enlargement

*There's an **important difference** between similarity and congruence.*

Q1 The side view of a playground swing is shown in the diagram. Triangles PQR and PST are similar.

a) Write down the distance PT.

b) Calculate the distance ST.

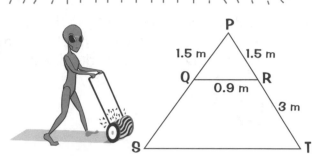

Q2 Two cups A and B are similar. Cup A has a height of 30 cm and cup B has a height of 20 cm. Cup A has a volume of 54 cm³. Calculate the volume of cup B.

 Don't forget that when you're enlarging areas and volumes, there's a bigger scale factor — that one catches everyone out, believe me...

Q3 A box of chocolates is to have the shape of a cuboid 15 cm long, 8 cm wide and 10 cm high.

a) Calculate the area of material needed to make the box (assuming no flaps are required for glueing).

b) In advertising the chocolates, the manufacturer decides he will have a box made in a similar shape. The enlargement is to have a scale factor of 50. Calculate the area of material required to make the box for publicity. Give your answer in square metres.

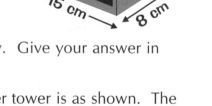

Q4

A scale model of a proposed water tower is as shown. The model is a cylinder of height 4 m and base radius 0.2 m. The proposed water level in the full size tower is 1000 m high.

a) What is the base radius of the full size tower?

b) Calculate, in cubic metres, the volume of the scale mode.

c) How many times larger than the scale model is the volume of the proposed water tower?

Q5 A boy made a symmetrical framework with metal rods as shown. Lengths AB = BC, ST = TC and AP = PQ. Angle BVC = 90° and length BV = 9 cm.

a) Find two triangles which are similar to triangle ABC.

b) Calculate the length of AP. Hence write down the length of PT.

c) Calculate the area of triangle ABC.

d) Find the area of triangle APQ. Give your answer correct to 3 significant figures.

e) Hence write down the area of PQBST correct to 2 significant figures.

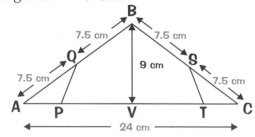

2.8 Questions on Similarity and Enlargement

Q6 Using the point O as centre of enlargement draw accurately and label:

a) the image $A_1B_1C_1$ of the triangle ABC after an enlargement scale factor 2

b) the image $A_2B_2C_2$ of the triangle ABC after an enlargement scale factor -1.

c) Which image is congruent to triangle ABC?

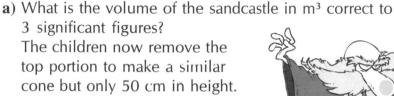

Q7 On a holiday near the sea, children built a sandcastle in the shape of a cone. The radius of the base is 100 cm and the height is 100 cm.

a) What is the volume of the sandcastle in m³ correct to 3 significant figures?
The children now remove the top portion to make a similar cone but only 50 cm in height.

b) State the radius of the base of this smaller cone.

c) State the ratio of the volume of the small cone to the volume of the original cone.

d) Calculate the volume of the small cone in m³ correct to 3 significant figures.

e) Hence write down the ratio of the volume of the portion left of the original cone to the smaller cone in the form n:1.

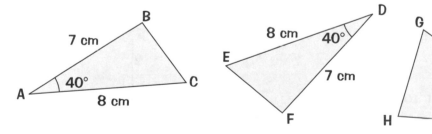

Q8 A cylindrical bottle contains 1 litre of oil. A second cylindrical bottle has twice the radius but the same height. It also contains oil.

a) Explain why these bottles are not similar.

b) How much oil is in the larger bottle?

Q9 Which pair of triangles is congruent. Give a reason for congruency.

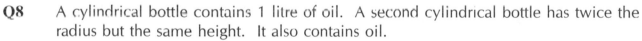

Q10 BC is parallel to DE. AB = 12 cm, BD = 8 cm, DE = 25 cm and CE = 10 cm.

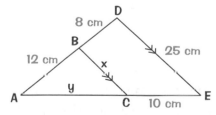

a) Explain why triangles ABC and ADE are similar.

b) Find the lengths of x and y in the diagram.

Q11 Another triangle, congruent to the given triangle, must be drawn with vertices at three of the dots. Show in how many different ways this can be done.

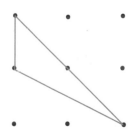

SECTION TWO — SHAPES

2.9 Questions on The Four Transformations

Only 4 of these to learn... and good old TERRY's always around to help if you need him.

Q1 Copy the axes and mark on triangle A with corners (-1, 2) (0, 4) and (-2, 4).

Use a scale of 1 cm to 1 unit.

a) Reflect A in the line y = -x.
Label this image B.

b) Reflect A in the line x = 1.
Label the image C.

c) Reflect A in the line y = -1.
Label the image D.

d) Translate triangle D with the vector $\begin{pmatrix} 4 \\ 2 \end{pmatrix}$. Label this image E.

e) Translate triangle C with the vector $\begin{pmatrix} 3 \\ -3 \end{pmatrix}$. Label this image F.

f) Describe fully the transformation that sends C to E.

g) Describe fully the transformation that sends F to A.

 Transformations... just about the most fun you can have without crying.

Q2 Copy the axes using a scale of 1 cm to 1 unit. Mark on the axes a quadrilateral Q with corners (-2, 1), (-3, 1), (-3, 3) and (-2, 3).

a) Rotate Q clockwise through 90° about the point (-1, 2). Label the image R.

b) Rotate R clockwise through 90° about the point (0, 1). Label the image S.

c) Describe fully the rotation that maps Q to S.

d) Describe fully the translation that sends Q to S.

e) Describe fully the reflection that sends Q to S.

f) Rotate Q through 180° about the point (-½, -1). Label the image T.

g) Rotate Q anticlockwise through 90° about the point (-1, -1). Label the image U.

h) Describe fully the rotation that sends U to T.

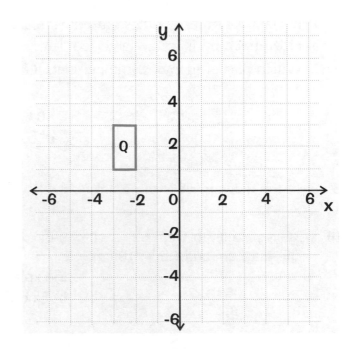

2.9 Questions on The Four Transformations

Move each point separately — then check your shape hasn't done anything unexpected while you weren't looking.

Q3 Copy the axes below using a scale of 1 cm to 1 unit.

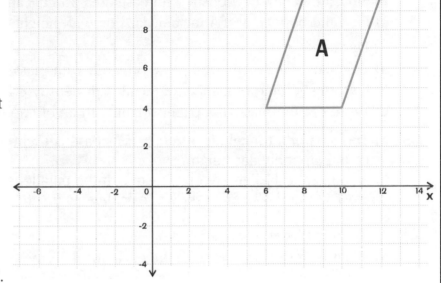

A parallelogram A has vertices at (6, 4) (10, 4) (8, 10) and (12, 10). Draw this parallelogram onto your axes. An enlargement scale factor 1/2 and centre (0,0) transforms parallelogram A onto its image B.

a) Draw this image B on your axes.

b) Translate B by the vector $\begin{pmatrix} -3 \\ -2 \end{pmatrix}$ and label this image C.

c) Calculate the ratio of the area of parallelogram C to the area of parallelogram A.

Q4 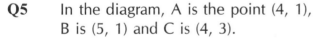 Draw axes with x and y running from 0 to 12 with a scale of 1 cm to 1 unit. O is the origin. $\overrightarrow{OP} = \begin{pmatrix} 4 \\ 2 \end{pmatrix}$, $\overrightarrow{PQ} = \begin{pmatrix} -1 \\ 2 \end{pmatrix}$, and $\overrightarrow{QR} = 2\overrightarrow{OP}$

a) Mark P, Q and R on your axes.

b) Calculate the lengths of the vectors $\overrightarrow{OP}$ and $\overrightarrow{OQ}$.

c) Find the equation of the line joining P and Q.

d) Give R the translation $\overrightarrow{QO}$. Label the image T.

e) Verify that the column vectors $\overrightarrow{PQ} + \overrightarrow{QR} + \overrightarrow{RT} + \overrightarrow{TP} = O$.

Urghh — vectors...
Make sure you get the coordinates the right way round — top for x dirⁿ, bottom for y dirⁿ.

Q5 In the diagram, A is the point (4, 1), B is (5, 1) and C is (4, 3).

a) Using a scale of 1cm to 1 unit draw the diagram and mark on it the figure given by ABC.

b) Reflect ABC in the X-axis and label the image $A_1B_1C_1$.

c) Reflect $A_1B_1C_1$ in the Y-axis and label the image $A_2B_2C_2$.

d) Describe fully the single transformation which would map ABC onto $A_2B_2C_2$.

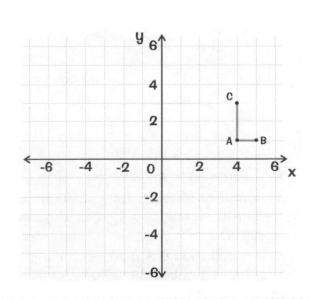

3.1 Questions on Formula Triangles

 This is what you've been waiting for all those years — pages of formula triangles... perhaps the most important bit of this section. Get the hang of these and everything will fall into place.

Q1 Volume = base area × height.
a) Find the volume of a cylinder with radius 3 cm and height 12 cm.
b) Find the height of a prism with base area 35 cm² and volume 400 cm³.
c) Find the base area of a rectangular box with height 25 cm and volume 1500 cm³.

Q2 Density = mass per unit volume.
a) Calculate the density of a piece of wood with mass 7.5 g and volume 11 cm³.
b) Find the volume of a sheet of metal with density 8.2 g/cm³ and mass 125 g.
c) Work out the mass of a paperweight with a volume 56 cm³ and density 9 g/cm³.

Q3 a) The area of a triangle is 34 cm². If its base is 6 cm, what is its perpendicular height?
b) A trapezium has an area of 50 cm². If the parallel sides are 7 cm and 12 cm as shown, calculate its height, h.

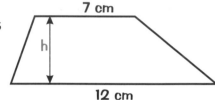

Q4 Volume of a sphere = $\frac{4}{3}\pi r^3$
a) What is the volume of a sphere of radius 4.2 cm?
b) What is the radius of a sphere with volume 60 cm³?
c) Calculate the diameter of a sphere of volume 100 cm³.

Q5 A circular table has a diameter of 1.5 m. A circular cloth is put on the table and hangs down 10 cm all round.
a) What is the radius of the cloth?
b) Binding is to be put around the edge of the cloth. How much will be needed if the ends overlap by 2 cm?

Q6 Trigonometry rules: $\tan\theta = \dfrac{o}{a}$, $\sin\theta = \dfrac{o}{h}$, $\cos\theta = \dfrac{a}{h}$

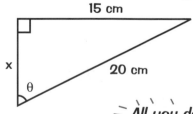

a) Calculate angle θ.
b) Find length x.
c) Work out the area of the triangle.

All you do is cover up the thing you want with your finger — the other 2 bits will tell you how to calculate it. Squeezy lemons.

Q7 A statue has a volume of 4 m³. The density of the stone used is 9.3 g/cm³.
a) Calculate the mass of the statue.
b) A replica of the statue is made in a lighter material with a density of only 3.5 g/cm³. What will be the weight of the replica?
c) A small model is made in the lighter material weighing just 5 kg. Calculate the volume of the model.

3.1 Questions on Formula Triangles

Q8 Gradient $= \dfrac{\text{height}}{\text{horizontal distance travelled}}$

a) The gradient of a hill is given as 4%. In a horizontal distance of 4 km how much height will be gained?

b) In driving a horizontal distance of 12 km, I climbed 25 m vertically. What was the average gradient?

c) A ramped kerbstone is 10 cm high. What will be the gradient of the slope to the top if it starts 26 cm away?

 You've got to be really careful when you're dealing with __formula triangles__ — remember, __the units you get out__ of a formula triangle __depend entirely on the units you put into it__.

Bits & Bobs Crossword

ACROSS

1) The standard way to learn this is to say, "times ten to the power". (4)
3) These describe both magnitude and direction. (7)
6) The angles of _____ and depression are equal. (9)
8) Unlike a British summer you're guaranteed one if you divide the opposite by the adjacent in a right-angled triangle. (3)
10) $a^2 + o^2 = h^2$, where a = adjacent, o = opposite and h = hypotenuse. (10)
11) A compass bearing due 090°. (4)

DOWN

2) If you break this you may get it wrong. (4)
4) So we click !!! (9)
5) -090° if you're facing West. (5)
7) An answer is incomplete unless it also has these. (5)
9) Learn how to use these triangles and you won't go wrong. (7)
12) Where the gradient of a line on a graph represents either acceleration or speed, you will find me on the axis. (4)

3.2 Questions on Speed, Distance and Time

 I reckon this is <u>pretty easy</u> — it's just a case of taking your time, putting the right numbers into the <u>speed formula triangle</u> and getting the answer out. And don't forget to check your answer's in the right units.

Q1 **a)** A car travels 32 km in 40 mins. What is its average speed?
   b) A train travels at an average speed of 96 km/hr for 35 mins. How far has it travelled?
   c) A cyclist travels 12 km at 16 km/hr. How long does it take?

Q2 A car travels 8 km at an average speed of 30 km/hr. Then it joins the motorway and travels 200 km at 104 km/hr.
What is the average speed for the whole journey?

Q3 A main road through a town has a speed limit of 30 mph. A driver covers 2¼ miles through the centre in 4 mins. Did she break the speed limit?

Q4 A train leaves station A at 0915 and arrives at station B at 1005. If it travels at an average speed of 72 mph, how far apart are the stations?

Q5 This table shows the car mileage at various times on a journey.

Time	1410	1530	1655	1845	2040
Mileage	10537	10589	10655	10695	10780

   a) What was the average speed between 1410 and 1530?
   b) Between which times do you think a stop was made for refuelling and refreshments? Give a reason.
   c) What was the average speed for the last section of the journey?
   d) If the car does approximately 12 miles per litre of fuel, how many litres are used on the journey?
   e) What was the average speed for the whole journey?

Q6 A cyclist leaves home at 1430 and cycles at an average speed of 14 km/hr to visit a friend. After one hour he stops for 20 mins then continues at an average speed of 11 km/hr and arrives at his friend's house at 1700.
   a) How far does he travel before the rest?
   b) How far is it to his friend's house?
   c) What was his average speed for the whole journey?

3.2   Questions on Speed, Distance and Time

Q7   The distance between two railway stations is 145 km.
  a) How long does a train travelling at 65 km/hr on average take to travel this distance?
  b) Another train travels at an average speed of 80 km/hr but has a 10 min stop during the journey. How long does this second train take?
  c) If both arrive at 1600, what time did each leave?

Q8   Two athletes run a road race. One ran at an average speed of 16 km/hr, the other at 4 m/sec. Which was the fastest? How long would each take to run 10 km?

Q9   A plane leaves Amsterdam at 0715 and flies at an average speed of 650 km/hr to Paris, arriving at 0800. It takes off again at 0840 and flies at the same average speed to Nice arriving at 1005.
  a) How far is it from Amsterdam to Paris?
  b) How far is it from Paris to Nice?
  c) What was the averge speed for the whole journey?

*Remember, for the average speed, you use the **total** time and the **total** distance.*

Q10   A runner covered the first 100 m of a 200 m race in 12.3 seconds.
  a) What was his average speed for the first 100 m?
  b) The second 100 m took 15.1 seconds. What was the average speed for 200 m?

Q11   A military plane can achieve a speed of 1100 km/hr. At this speed it passes over town A at 1205 and town B at 1217.
  a) How far apart are towns A and B?
  b) The plane then flies over village C which is 93 km from B. How long does it take from B to C?

Q12   Two cars set off on 180 mile journeys. One travels mostly on A roads and manages an average speed of 42 mph. The other car travels mostly on the motorway and achieves an average speed of 64 mph. If they both take the same time over the journey, for how long does the second car stop?

Q13   A stone is dropped from a cliff top. After 1 second it has fallen 4.8 m, after 2 seconds a total of 19.2 m and after 3 seconds 43.2 m. Calculate its average speed in:
  a) the first second
  b) the second second
  c) for all 3 seconds
  d) Change all the m/sec speeds to km/hr.

Q14   In 1990 three motor racers had fastest lap times of 236.6, 233.8 and 227.3 km/hr. If 1 km = 0.62 miles, how long would each driver take to lap 5 miles?

3.3 Questions on D/T graphs and V/T graphs

You need to remember what the different bits of a travel graph mean — what it looks like when **stopped**, **changing speed** and **coming back** to the starting point.

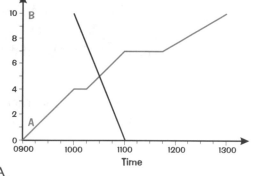

Q1 Peter set out from A at 0900 to walk to B.

a) How far did he walk in the 1st hour?

b) He stopped twice; how long was each stop?

c) What was his speed after the second stop?

At 1000 Sarah set out on her bike to ride from B to A.

d) What time did she arrive at A?

e) What was her average speed?

f) At what time did Peter and Sarah pass each other?

Q2 Mr. Smith leaves home at 0730 to go to work. He walks at a steady 6 km/hr for 2 km. He catches the 0755 train which takes 35 mins to travel 50 km. He then walks 3 km to work and arrives at 0900. Draw a graph to show this. How long did he wait at the station for the train?

Q3 This graph shows a return bus journey between Kendal and Sedbergh.

a) How long was the first stop?

b) How long was the second stop?

c) How far did it travel in the first 10 mins?

d) What was the average speed for the journey from Sedbergh to Kendal?

e) What was its fastest speed?

f) What was the average speed for the whole journey?

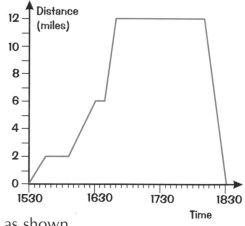

Q4 On sports day the first three in the 1000 m race ran as shown.

a) Which runner A, B or C won the race?

b) How long did the winner take?

c) Which runner kept up a steady speed?

d) What was that speed
 i) in m/min?
 ii) km/hr?

e) Which runner achieved the fastest speed and what was that speed?

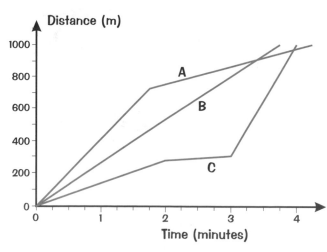

3.3 Questions on D/T graphs and V/T graphs

Q5 This diagram shows the different times taken by 5 trains to travel 100 km.

a) Calculate the speed of each train.

b) How could you tell by looking at the diagram which was the fastest and which the slowest?

c) Train D should have been travelling at 50 km/hr. How many minutes late was it?

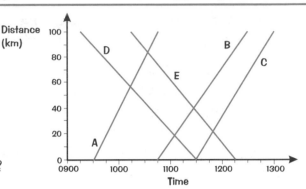

Q6 Two cars start a journey at midday (1200) — one from town A and the other from village B. A and B are 80 km apart. The car from town A travels at an average speed of 48 km/hr and the other car, from village B, at 60 km/hr.

a) Draw a graph to show these journeys.

b) At what time do the cars pass? (approx.)

c) How far from A are they when they pass?

Q7 A plane flies from P to Q and after refuelling flies on to R. This table gives details of the flight.

Time from P (hrs)	0	1	2	3	4	5	6
Distance from P (km)	0	900	1800	2700	2700	3400	4100

a) Draw a graph to show this journey.

b) What was the average speed from P to Q?

c) What was the average speed from Q to R?

d) At what time was the plane 2000 km from P if it left at 0825?

Remember that the gradient of the graph is the speed. When you're drawing these graphs, make sure you choose sensible units for your axes, and when you read off the answer, remember to use those units. Don't just measure it in cm!

Q8 A girl sets off on an all-day walk. She started at 0915 and walked at a steady speed for 9 km before stopping at 1100 for a 20 min break. She then set off again at a steady speed and walked 8 km, stopping at 1300 for 45 mins. After lunch she walked at 3½ km/hr for 2½ hrs to her destination.

a) Draw a graph to show this walk.

b) How far did she walk altogether?

c) What was the average speed for the whole walk?

d) What was her fastest walking speed?

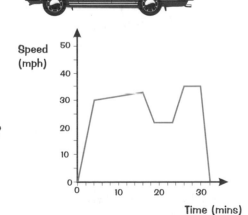

Q9 This graph shows a car journey.

a) How long did the journey last?

b) How often did it travel at a steady speed?

c) For how many minutes was it travelling over 30 mph?

d) During which times was the acceleration greatest?

e) How long did it take to slow down at the end?

f) What was the fastest speed achieved?

3.3 Questions on D/T graphs and V/T graphs

These questions have always got loads of bits to them, so make sure you're happy with how the graphs work before you start.

Q10 A train starts from rest at X and increases its speed at a steady rate for three minutes until it reaches 90 km/hr. It maintains this speed for 15 mins, then slows down steadily at a rate of 18 km/hr per minute until it comes to a stop at Y.

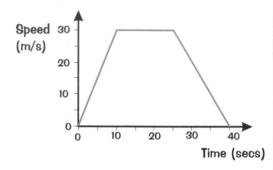

a) Draw a speed/time graph to show this train journey.

b) How far does the train travel at its highest speed?

c) What is the speed of the train after 1 minute?

d) When does the train next travel at this speed?

Q11 This speed/time graph shows a train journey between stops.

a) How long did it take the train to achieve 30 m/s?

b) How long was the journey?

c) How far was it between stops?

d) What was the average speed for the journey?

Q12 A train starts from rest and increases speed steadily over the first 80 seconds to 18 m/s. It then immediately starts to slow down, coming to a stop after a total journey of 140 seconds.

a) Draw a speed/time graph to show this.

b) What is the speed after 1 minute?

c) What is the total distance travelled?

Q13 This diagram shows a day trip on a boat.

a) Work out the total distance travelled.

b) Calculate the average speed for the whole day.

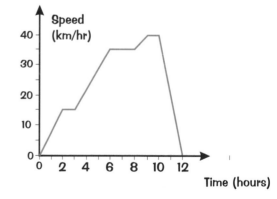

Q14 An aircraft took off and accelerated uniformly to 800 km/hr in the first 5 minutes. It maintained this speed for 20 mins and then steadily increased again to 1000 km/hr over the next 3 minutes.

a) Draw a speed/time graph to show this.

b) What was the speed after 2 minutes?

c) How far has the plane gone after 25 minutes?

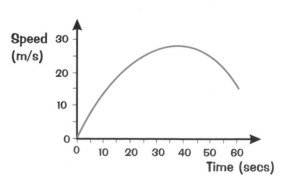

Q15 This curved graph shows the speed of a car during the first minute of its journey.

a) When did the car start accelerating?

b) When did the car start to slow down?

c) Estimate the speed after 20 seconds.

d) Approximately how far had the car gone in one minute?

3.3 Questions on D/T graphs and V/T graphs

Don't worry — there's never anything too tricky in here and they're all pretty much the same — if you can do one, you can do them all.

Q16 This table shows the velocity achieved by a particle.

Time (seconds)	0	0.5	1	1.5	2	2.5	3
Velocity (m/s)	0	5.6	8.8	10.5	12	11.4	10

a) Draw a velocity/time graph.

b) How far had the particle travelled after 2 seconds?

c) What was the average acceleration in the first 0.5 seconds?

Q17 This diagram shows how a cyclist rode part of a race. Calculate:

a) the acceleration between 0 and 10 mins

b) the deceleration between 20 and 25 mins

c) the total distance travelled in 35 mins

d) the average speed for the first 30 mins.

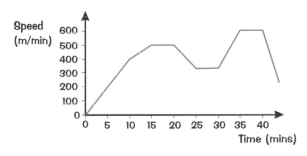

Q18 A car accelerates steadily from rest to a speed of 100 km/hr, taking 25 seconds to do this.

a) Draw a speed/time graph to show this.

b) Estimate the total distance covered.

Q19 The speeds of a train were recorded as shown.

Time (minutes)	0	2	4	6	8	10
Speed (km/hr)	0	35	52	78	69	75

a) Draw a speed/time graph as a smooth curve.

b) How long after starting did it achieve 70 km/hr?

c) When next did it achieve this speed?

d) How far did it travel in 10 minutes?

Q20 Two vehicles start from rest at the same time. One accelerates steadily at a rate of 0.65 m/sec^2. The other accelerates as shown in the table.

Time (seconds)	0	2	4	6	8	10	12	14
Speed (m/s)	0	1	1.5	2.3	3.2	5.5	7.8	10

a) Draw these speed/time graphs on the same axes.

b) Estimate when both vehicles travel at the same speed.

c) Is there any difference in the distance travelled by each?

3.4 Questions on Standard Index Form

Writing very big (or very small) numbers gets a bit messy with all those zeros, if you don't use this standard index form. But of course, the main reason for knowing about standard form is...you guessed it — it's in the Exam.

Q1 Write as ordinary numbers:
- **a)** 3.56×10
- **b)** 3.56×10^3
- **c)** 3.56×10^{-1}
- **d)** 3.56×10^4
- **e)** 0.082×10^2
- **f)** 0.082×10^{-2}
- **g)** 0.082×10
- **h)** 0.082×10^{-1}
- **i)** 157×10
- **j)** 157×10^{-3}
- **k)** 157×10^3
- **l)** 157×10^{-1}.

Q2 Write in standard form:
- **a)** 2.56
- **b)** 25.6
- **c)** 0.256
- **d)** 25600
- **e)** 95.2
- **f)** 0.0952
- **g)** 95 200
- **h)** 0.000952
- **i)** 4200
- **j)** 0.0042
- **k)** 42
- **l)** 420.

Q3 Write in standard form:
- **a)** 34.7×10
- **b)** 73.004
- **c)** 0.005×10^3
- **d)** 9183×10^2
- **e)** 15 million
- **f)** 937.1×10^4
- **g)** 0.000075
- **h)** 0.05×10^{-2}
- **i)** 534×10^{-2}
- **j)** 621.03
- **k)** 149×10^2
- **l)** 0.003×10^{-4} .

Q4 Calculate and give your answers in standard form:
- **a)** $(3.7 \times 10^2) \times (1.4 \times 10^4)$
- **b)** $(0.5 \times 10^3) \times (8.1 \times 10^2)$
- **c)** $(0.03 \times 10^{-1}) \times (5.6 \times 10^{-2})$
- **d)** $(3.9 \times 10^2) \div (2.7 \times 10)$
- **e)** $(0.7 \times 10^4) \div (1.5 \times 10^2)$
- **f)** $(8.21 \times 10^5) \div (0.4 \times 10^3)$.

Q5 Calculate and give your answers in standard form:
- **a)** $(4.5 \times 10^2)^2$
- **b)** $\sqrt{4.9 \times 10^3}$
- **c)** $\dfrac{0.534 \times 10^{-1}}{2.3 \times 10^{-4}}$
- **d)** $\dfrac{4 \times 10^{-2}}{8 \times 10^{-3}}$
- **e)** $(2.86 \times 10^{-3})^2$
- **f)** $\sqrt{0.36 \times 10^{-2}}$.

Q6 Calculate the following, writing your answer as an ordinary decimal number:
- **a)** $(2.4 \times 10^2) \div (1.5 \times 10)$
- **b)** $(0.5 \times 10^{-1}) \times (3.2 \times 10^{-2})$
- **c)** $(3.7 \times 10^4) \div (5.6 \times 10^3)$
- **d)** $(0.03 \times 10^3) \times (0.71 \times 10^{-2})$
- **e)** $256.3 \div (0.19 \times 10^2)$
- **f)** $(2.76 \times 10^{-2}) \times 576$
- **g)** $0.003 \times (2.4 \times 10^2)$
- **h)** $(1.98 \times 10^{-4}) \div 0.0004$
- **i)** $2,468 \times (0.9 \times 10^{-3})$
- **j)** $(3.7 \times 10^{-5}) \div (1.5 \times 10^4)$.

Don't forget that if it's a negative power, you move the decimal point the other way.

3.4   Questions on Standard Index Form

Write the numbers in Questions 7 to 11 in standard form.

Q7 The distance between Paris and Rome is 1476 km.

Q8 A rectangular field is 24,700 cm by 15,000 cm. What is its perimeter in m²?

Q9 A billion = a million million   A trillion = a million million million.

Q10 A light year is 9,460,000,000,000 km (approx).

Q11 Nautilus covered 69,138 miles before having to refuel.

Give all answers to subsequent questions in standard form.

Q12 The density of a liquid is 1.25×10^3 kg/m³. What is the volume of 500 g of this liquid?

Q13 This table gives the diameter and distance from the Sun of some planets.

Planet	Distance from Sun (km)	Diameter (km)
Earth	1.5×10^8	1.3×10^4
Venus	1.085×10^8	1.2×10^4
Mars	2.28×10^8	6.8×10^3
Mercury	5.81×10^7	4.9×10^3
Jupiter	7.8×10^8	1.4×10^5
Neptune	4.52×10^9	4.9×10^4
Saturn	1.43×10^9	1.2×10^5

From the table write down which planet is:
a) smallest in diameter
b) largest in diameter
c) nearest to the Sun
d) furthest from the Sun.

Write down which planets are:
e) nearer to the Sun than the Earth
f) bigger in diameter than the Earth.

Q14 Quartz vibrates at about 2.5 million pulses each second.
Caesium vibrates at about 9,192,631,770 vibrations per second.
a) Write both these numbers in standard form.
b) Calculate how many more times per second caesium vibrates than quartz.

Q15 The distance of some cities from Calais is given in this table.

City	distance in km from Calais
Amsterdam	360
Barcelona	1326
Hamburg	714
Helsinki	1867
Madrid	1558
Marseille	1011

a) Write all the distances in standard form.
Work out which city is:
b) closest to Calais
c) furthest from Calais
d) approximately twice as far from Calais as Hamburg.
e) What is the ratio of the distance between Calais and Barcelona to that between Calais and Madrid?

Q16 One hour = 60 minutes   One minute = 60 seconds.
Write in standard form the number of seconds in an hour.
a) What is the speed in km/sec of a plane flying at 8.7×10^2 km/hr?
b) The speed of light is approximately 3.0×10^8 m/sec. Write this in km/hr.

Q17 The mass of the Moon is about 0.0123 times that of the Earth. If the mass of the Earth is 5.974×10^{21} tonnes, calculate the mass of the Moon to 3 s.f.

You may have noticed standard form is used a lot in science, so if you're a budding nuclear physicist, get learning. Oh, you're not. Well, you've still got to learn it. Sorry.

3.5 Questions on Powers and Roots

Hang on there. Before you try this page, make sure you know the 7 easy rules — and the 3 tricky ones... they'll be on P.36 of the Revision Guide if you want them.

For Questions 1 to 5 answers should be given to 3 s.f.

Q1
a) $(6.5)^3$
b) $(0.35)^2$
c) $(15.2)^4$
d) $(0.04)^3$

e) $\sqrt{5.6}$
f) $\sqrt[3]{12.4}$
g) $\sqrt{109}$
h) $\sqrt[3]{0.6}$

i) $(1\frac{1}{2})^2$
j) $\sqrt{4\frac{3}{4}}$
k) $\left(\frac{5}{8}\right)^3$
l) $\sqrt[3]{\frac{9}{10}}$

> *There are always two possible square roots — a positive one and a negative one.*
> *So remember to stick the ± sign in front of your answer.*

Q2
a) $(2.4)^2 + 3$
b) $5.9 - (1.2)^3$
c) $\sqrt[3]{5.6} + (4.2)^2$

d) $(6.05)^3 - \sqrt[3]{8.4}$
e) $6.1[35.4 - (4.2)^2]$
f) $95 - 3(\sqrt[3]{48} - 2.6)$

g) $1\frac{1}{2}[4 + (2\frac{1}{4})^2]$
h) $19 - 4[(\frac{1}{4})^2 + ((\frac{5}{8})^3)]$
i) $15\frac{3}{5} - 2\frac{1}{2}[(1\frac{3}{4})^3 - \sqrt[3]{1\frac{1}{2}}]$

Q3
a) 5^{-3}
b) 2^{-2}
c) 16^{-4}
d) $(1.5)^{-1}$

e) $5^{\frac{1}{2}}$
f) $6^{\frac{1}{3}}$
g) $9^{\frac{1}{5}}$
h) $(4.2)^{\frac{2}{3}}$

i) $(1\frac{1}{4})^{-3}$
j) $(2\frac{3}{5})^{\frac{1}{5}}$
k) $(5\frac{1}{3})^{-2}$
l) $(10\frac{5}{6})^{\frac{5}{6}}$

Q4 Use the positive value of any square roots in these calculations:

a) $\sqrt{(1.4)^2 + (0.5)^2}$

b) $5.9[(2.3)^{\frac{1}{4}} + (4.7)^{\frac{1}{2}}]$

c) $2.5 - 0.6[(7.1)^{-3} - (9.5)^{-4}]$

d) $(8.2)^{-2} + (1.6)^4 - (3.7)^{-3}$

e) $\dfrac{3\sqrt{8} - 2}{6}$

f) $\dfrac{15 + 3\sqrt{4.1}}{2.4}$

g) $3\sqrt{4.7} - 4\sqrt{2.1}$

h) $\dfrac{(2\frac{1}{4})^{-2} - (3\frac{1}{2})^{\frac{1}{2}}}{4.4}$

Q5 Use the positive value of any square roots in these calculations:

a) $(2\frac{1}{4})^3 - (1.5)^2$

b) $(3.7)^{-2} + (4\frac{1}{5})^{\frac{1}{4}}$

c) $\sqrt[3]{5\frac{1}{3}} \times (4.3)^{-1}$

d) $(7.4)^{\frac{1}{3}} \times (6\frac{1}{4})^3$

e) $\dfrac{\sqrt{22\frac{1}{2}} + (3.4)^2}{(6.9)^3 \times 3.4}$

f) $\dfrac{(15\frac{3}{5})^2 \times (2.5)^{-3}}{3 \times 4\frac{1}{4}}$

g) $5[(4.3)^2 - (2.5)^{\frac{1}{2}}]$

h) $\dfrac{3.5(2\frac{1}{6} - \sqrt{4.1})}{(3.5)^2 \times (3\frac{1}{2})^{-2}}$

i) $\dfrac{1\frac{1}{2} + \frac{1}{4}[(2\frac{2}{3})^2 - (1.4)^2]}{(3.9)^{-3}}$

j) $\sqrt[3]{2.73} + 5\sqrt{2}$

Remember, the power ½ means a square root.

3.5 Questions on Powers and Roots

Q6 Using the formula $V = \frac{4}{3}\pi r^3$:
a) find V if r = 1.4
b) find r if V = 32.

Q7 Using the formula $s = \frac{v^2 - u^2}{2a}$, find s if:
a) $v = 1\frac{2}{3}$, $u = \frac{5}{6}$, a = 3
b) v = 5.6, u = 3.4, a = 2.1.

Q8 Given that p = 2.3, q = 3½, r = −1.2, calculate:
a) $p^2 + q^3$
b) $p^{-2} + q^{½} + r^2$
c) $(p + q)^2 - r^{\frac{1}{3}}$
d) $p^{\frac{2}{3}} - q^{\frac{1}{3}}$
e) $(q - r)^3 - p^4$
f) $q^{\frac{2}{3}} + r^{\frac{1}{4}}$
g) $q^{-2} + r^3$
h) $p^{-2} + q^{½} - r^3$.

Q9 Jane wanted to calculate $\left(\frac{4.8 + 1.27}{1.2}\right)^2$

She got the answer 34.320069, which is incorrect.
a) Find the correct answer.
b) Suggest a reason for her getting it incorrect.

Q10 Using the formula $y = \frac{x - t}{\sqrt{1- v^2}}$

Find y when:
a) x = 40, t = 2, v = 0.5
b) x = 35.6, t = 1.45, v = ¼.

Q11 Using the formula s = ut + ½at²:
a) find s if u = 1.2, t = 5 and a = 2½
b) find u if s = 15.6, t = 0.3 and a = 2
c) find a if s = 25, u = 10 and t = 0.5.

Q12 Using the formula E = ½v² + gh:
a) find E if v = 4.2, g = 9.8 and h = −12.9
b) find g if E = 63, v = 4½ and h = 5.3
c) find v if E = 114, g = 7.5 and h = 2¾.

3.6 Questions on Pythagoras and Bearings

Don't try and do it all in your head — you've got to label the sides or you're bound to mess it up. Go on, get your pen out...

Q1 Find the length of the hypotenuse in each of the following triangles.

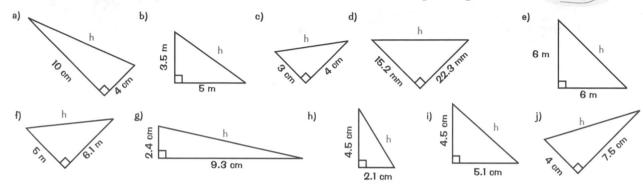

Q2 Find the length of the shorter side in each of the following triangles.

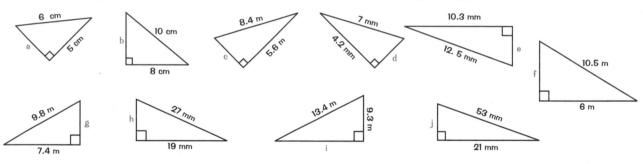

Q3 Find the unknown length in each of the following triangles.

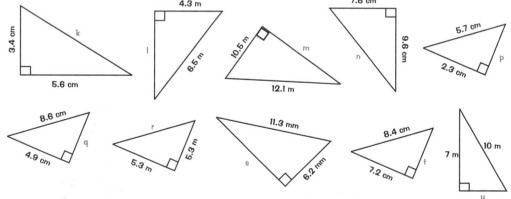

Q4 Find the bearings required in these diagrams.

It's easy to get lost if you don't follow the easy rule: always measure bearings from the __North Line__.

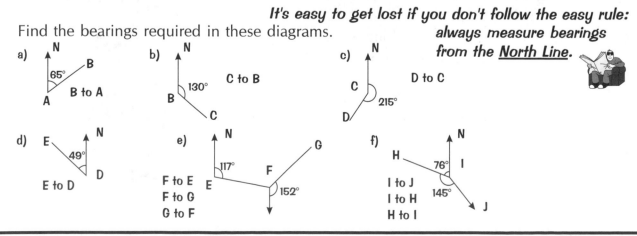

3.6 Questions on Pythagoras and Bearings

Q5 A ladder 11 m long leans against a wall. If the foot of the ladder is 6.5 m from the wall, how far up the wall will it reach?

Q6 A rectangular field is 250 m by 190 m. How far is it across diagonally?

Q7 **a)** Calculate the lengths WY and ZY.
b) What is the total distance WXYZW?
c) What is the area of quadrilateral WXYZ?

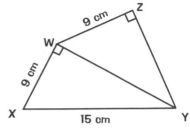

 The word "from" is the most important word in a bearings question, so look out for it — it tells you where to start from.

Q8 A plane flies due East for 153 km then turns and flies due North for 116 km. How far is it now from where it started?

Q9 A square tablecloth has a diagonal measurement of 130 cm. What is the length of one side?

Q10 A flagpole 10 m high is supported by metal wires each 11 m long. How far from the foot of the pole must the wires be fastened to the ground if the other end is attached to the top of the pole?

Q11 A coastguard spots a boat on a bearing of 040° and at a distance of 350 m. He can also see a tree due East of him. If the tree is due South of the boat, measure accurately the distances of the:
a) boat to the tree
b) coastguard to the tree.
c) Check by Pythagoras to see if your answers are reasonable.

By the time you've finished this section, you'll never be able to get lost. No matter how many times people tell you to.

Q12 Four towns W, X, Y and Z are situated thus:
W is 90 km North of X, Y is on a bearing 175° and 165 km from X, X is on a bearing 129° and 123 km from Z. Draw an accurate scale diagram to represent the situation. From your drawing measure the distances:
a) WZ   **b)** WY   **c)** ZY.
Measure the bearings:
d) Y from Z   **e)** W from Z   **f)** Y from W.

Q13 A walker travels 1200 m on a bearing of 165° and then another 1500 m on a bearing of 210°. By accurate measurement find how far she is now from her starting point. What bearing must she walk on to return to base?

Q14 A fishing boat travels at 12 km/hr for an hour due North. It then turns due West and travels at 7 km/hr for an hour. How far is it from its starting point now? What bearing must it travel on to return to base?

Q15 This pyramid is on a square base of side 56 cm. Its vertical height is 32 cm. Calculate the length of:
a) the line E to the mid point of BC
b) the sloping edge BE.

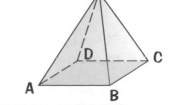

3.6   Questions on Pythagoras and Bearings

Q16   A 4½ m ladder is put up against a wall to just reach a window 2.5 m from the ground. How far away from the base of the wall must the bottom of the ladder be?

Q17   A plane flies from A to B on a bearing of 155° a distance of 240 km. C is due South of A and 315 km from A. From a scale drawing measure:

a) the bearing of C from B

b) the bearing of B from C

c) distance BC.

d) If the plane flies from A to B to C and back to A, calculate the total distance flown.

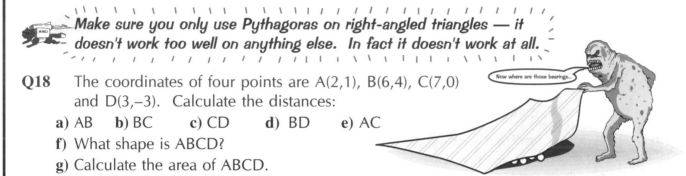

Make sure you only use Pythagoras on right-angled triangles — it doesn't work too well on anything else. In fact it doesn't work at all.

Now where are those bearings..

Q18   The coordinates of four points are A(2,1), B(6,4), C(7,0) and D(3,−3). Calculate the distances:

a) AB   b) BC   c) CD   d) BD   e) AC

f) What shape is ABCD?

g) Calculate the area of ABCD.

Q19   A ship sails on a bearing of 300° for 185 km. It is now 110 km due West of a lighthouse. By measuring from a scale drawing find its distance and bearing from the lighthouse when it started its journey.

Q20   Find the area of an isosceles triangle with these side measurements:

a) 4 cm, 4 cm, 4 cm

b) 9.5 cm, 9.5 cm, 10 cm

c) 15.3 cm, 15.3 cm, 22.7 cm.

Oops — no pictures... guess you'd better draw your own then.

Q21   Calculate the area of a regular hexagon with side 6 cm.

Q22   A rectangular box measures 20 cm by 30 cm by 8 cm. Calculate the lengths of:

a) the diagonal of each rectangular face

b) the diagonal through the centre of the box.

Q23   Rubber chocks are put under the wheels of aeroplanes to stop them moving when on the ground. A typical chock for a large aircraft is shown opposite.

a) Calculate the volume of rubber.

b) Calculate the mass of the chock if a rubber compound of density 1.7 g/cm^3 was used.

c) Would a person be able to lift this into position?

20cm
35cm
50cm
40cm

Q24   A corridor is 2.5 m wide and has a right angle bend in it as shown.

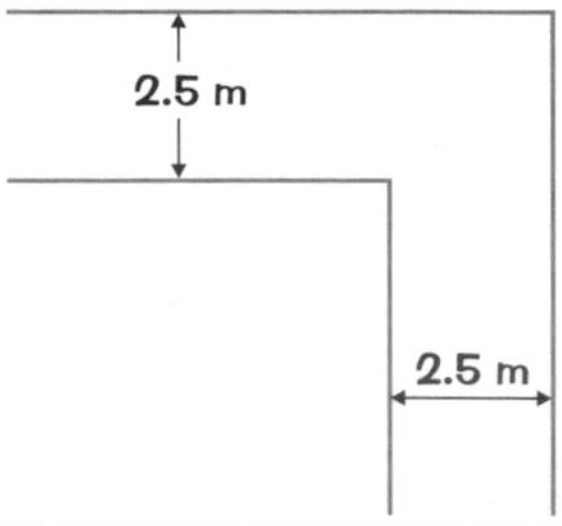

a) What is the longest ladder that can be carried horizontally along this corridor?

b) If the corridor is 3.5 m high, what is the longest ladder that can be carried along it in any direction?

2.5 m

2.5 m

3.7   Questions on Trigonometry

Before you start a trigonometry question, write down the ratios, using SOH CAH TOA (Sockatoa!) — it'll help you pick your formula triangle.

Q1   Use the tangent ratio to find the unknowns:

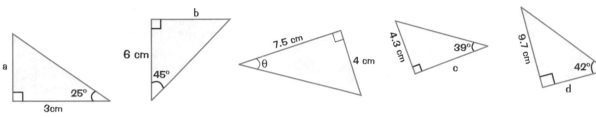

Q2   Use the cosine ratio to find the unknowns:

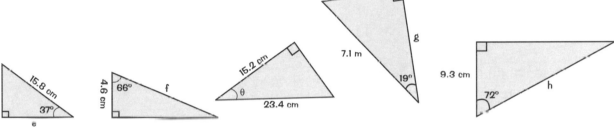

Q3   Use the sine ratio to find the unknowns:

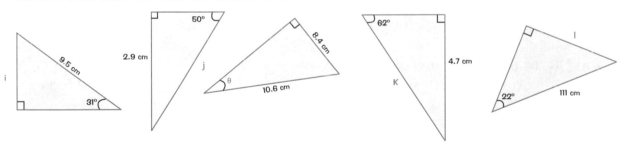

Q4   Find the unknowns using the appropriate ratios:

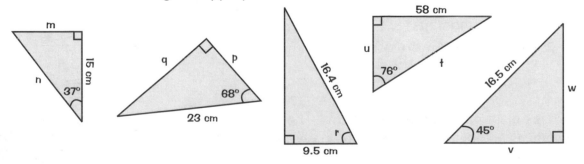

Q5   Calculate the tan, sin and cos of each of these angles:
    a) $17°$ **b)** $83°$ **c)** $5°$ **d)** $28°$ **e)** $45°$.

3.7   *Questions on Trigonometry*

Q6   Which angles have a tangent of:
     a) 2.43   **b)**   0.56?
     Which angles have a sine of:
     c) 0.56   **d)**   0.31?
     Which angles have a cosine of:
     e) 0.56   **f)**   0.31?

Make sure you've got the hang of the <u>*inverse*</u> *SIN, COS and TAN functions on your calc... and check it's in* <u>*DEG mode*</u> *or you'll get nowhere fast.*

Q7   Calculate the height of the tree using the measurements in the diagram.

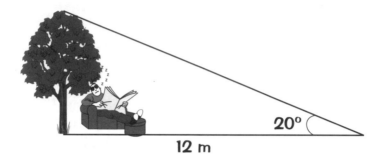

20°

12 m

Q8   This isosceles triangle has a base of 28 cm and a top angle of 54°. Calculate:
     a) the length of sides AC and BC
     b) the perpendicular height to C
     c) the area of the triangle.

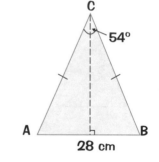

Q9   In this parallelogram the diagonal CB is at right angles to AC. AB is 9.5 cm and ∠CAB is 60°. Calculate:
     a) CB   **b)** BD   **c)** the area of the parallelogram.

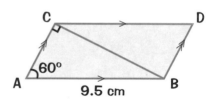

Q10   This rhombus WXYZ has base 15 cm and diagonal WY of 28 cm. Calculate the:
     a) length of diagonal XZ
     b) area of the rhombus
     c) angle WY makes with WX.

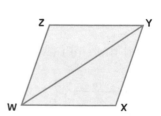

Q11   This glass has a radius of 2.8 cm. The straw in the glass makes an angle of 70° with the base and protrudes 4 cm above the rim.
     a) How tall is the glass?
     b) How long is the straw?

glug glug glug

4cm

70°

3.7   Questions on Trigonometry

Don't let that circle put you off — it's a normal question really.
Just label the sides and you're away...

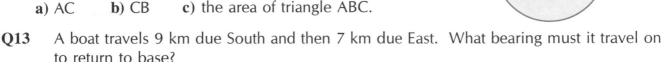

Q12   AOB is the diameter of a circle of radius 6 cm.
∠ACB is a right angle. Calculate:

   a) AC   **b)** CB   **c)** the area of triangle ABC.

Q13   A boat travels 9 km due South and then 7 km due East. What bearing must it travel on to return to base?

Q14   An isosceles triangle has two equal sides of 7 cm and an angle between them of 65°. Calculate the area of the triangle.

Q15   A 12 m ladder is placed against a wall and reaches 8.5 m up the wall. Calculate:

   a) how far the base of the ladder is from the wall

   b) the angle the ladder makes with the ground.

Q16   A girl who is 1.3 m tall flies a kite on a string of 45 m. The string of the kite makes an angle of 33° with the horizontal. What is the vertical height of the kite from the ground?

Q17   I am standing on top of an 80 m high tower. I look due North and see two cars with angles of depression of 38° and 49°. Calculate:

   a) how far each car is from the base of the tower

   b) how far apart the cars are.

Q18   A ship sails on a bearing of 300° for 100 km. The captain can then see a lighthouse due South of him that he knows is due west of his starting point. Calculate how far west the lighthouse is from the ship's starting point.

Q19   Two mountains are 1020 m and 1235 m high. Standing on the summit of the lower one I look up through an angle of elevation of 16° to see the summit of the higher one. Calculate the horizontal distance between the two mountains.

Q20

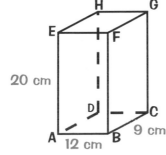

This rectangular box is 20 cm by 12 cm by 9 cm. Calculate:

   a) angle ∠FAB

   b) length AF

   c) length DF

   d) angle ∠AFD.

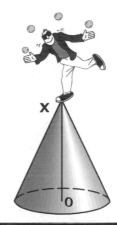

Q21   This cone has a perpendicular height of 9 cm. The centre of the base is O. The slant line from X makes an angle of 23° with the central axis. Calculate:

   a) the radius of the base

   b) the area of the base

   c) the volume of the cone.

3.8 Questions on The Sine and Cosine Rules

Make sure you know the Sine Rule and <u>both forms</u> of the Cosine Rule. You won't stand a chance in the exam otherwise.

Q1 Calculate the lengths required to 3 s.f.

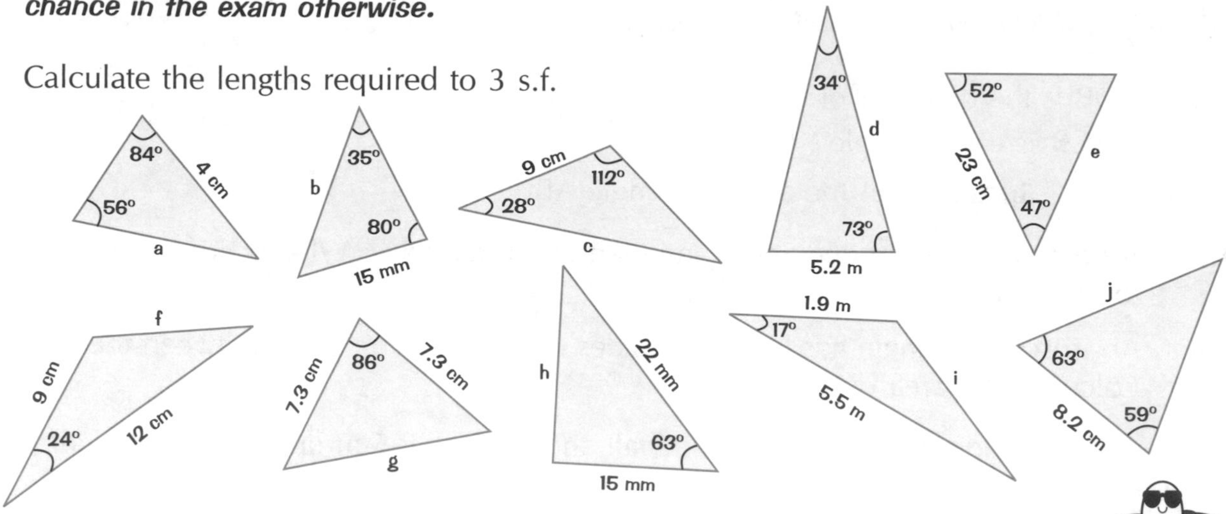

84°
56°
4 cm
a

35°
b
80°
15 mm

9 cm
112°
28°
c

34°
d
73°
5.2 m

52°
23 cm
47°
e

f
9 cm
24°
12 cm

7.3 cm
86°
7.3 cm
g

h
22 mm
63°
15 mm

1.9 m
17°
5.5 m
i

j
63°
8.2 cm
59°

Q2 Calculate the angles required, to the nearest degree.

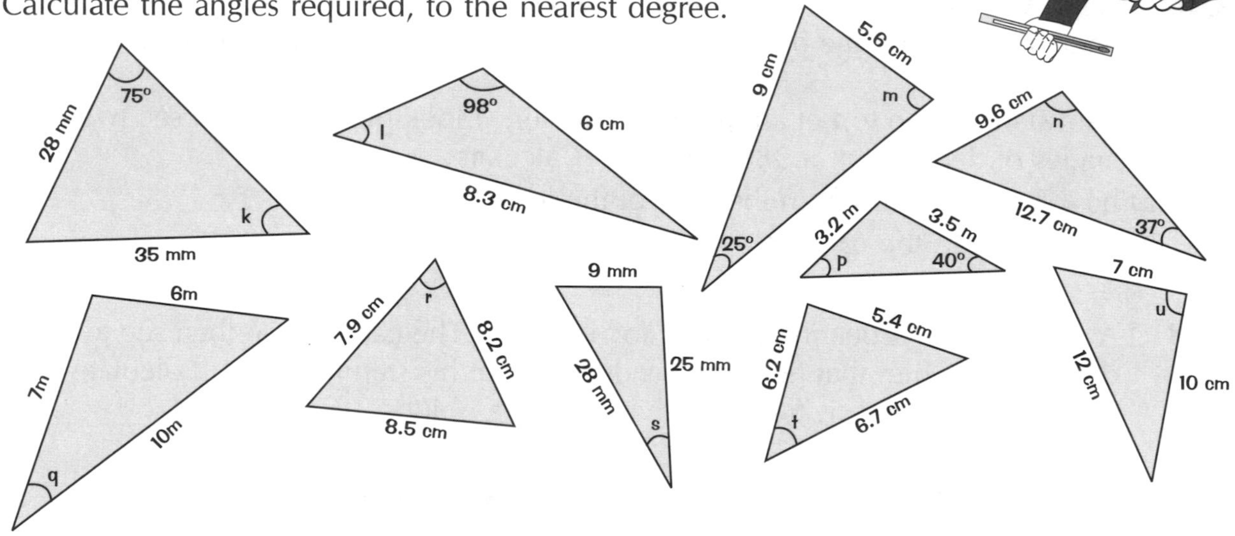

75°
28 mm
35 mm
k

98°
l
6 cm
8.3 cm

9 cm
5.6 cm
m
25°

9.6 cm
n
12.7 cm
37°

6m
7m
10m
q

7.9 cm
r
8.2 cm
8.5 cm

9 mm
28 mm
25 mm
s

3.2 m
P
3.5 m
40°

6.2 cm
5.4 cm
t
6.7 cm

7 cm
u
12 cm
10 cm

Q3 Calculate the lettered sides and angles.

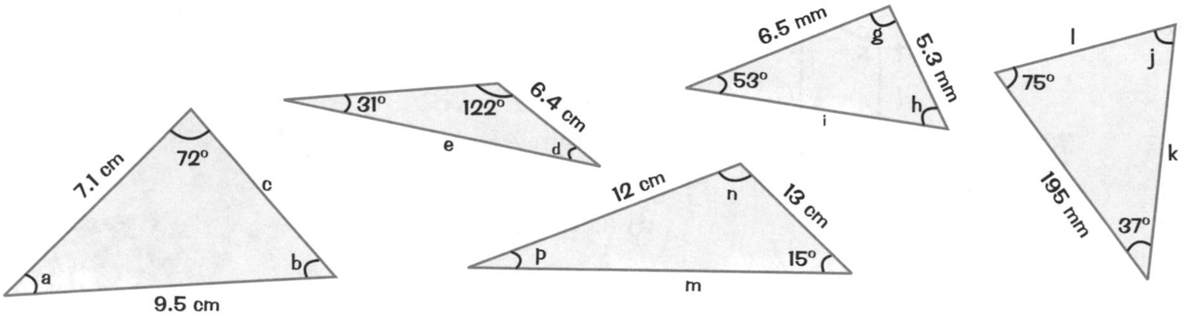

7.1 cm
72°
c
a
b
9.5 cm

31°
122°
6.4 cm
e
d

6.5 mm
g
5.3 mm
53°
h
i

l
75°
j
k
195 mm
37°

12 cm
n
13 cm
p
15°
m

Q4 Peter is standing on a bridge over a river. He can see a tree on each bank, one 33 m and the other 35 m away from him. If he looks through an angle of 20° going from one tree to the other, how far apart are the two trees?

3.8 Questions on The Sine and Cosine Rules

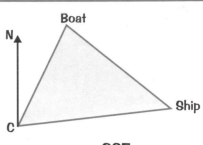

Q5 A coastguard sees a boat on a bearing of 038° from him and 25 km away. He also sees a ship 42 km away and on a bearing of 080°. Calculate:
a) the distance of the boat from the ship
b) the bearing of the boat from the ship.

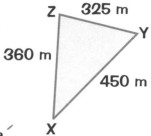

Q6 This field has measurements as shown. Calculate:
a) ∠ZXY
b) ∠XYZ
c) ∠YZX .

If you don't know which to use, try the Sine Rule first, because it's easier. Normally you won't have much choice, though.

Q7 An isosceles triangle has equal sides of length 7.5 cm and an angle of 56°. Sketch two possible triangles using this information and calculate the two answers for the length of the third side.

Q8 A parallelogram has sides of length 8 cm and 4.5 cm. One angle of the parallelogram is 124°. Calculate the lengths of the two diagonals.

Q9 On my clock the hour hand is 5.5 cm, the minute hand 8 cm and the second hand 7 cm, measured from the centre. Calculate the distance between the tips of the:
a) hour and minute hands at 10 o'clock
b) minute and second hands 15 seconds before 20 past the hour
c) hour and minute hands at 1020.

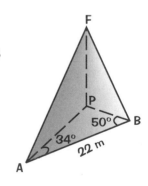

Q10 A vertical flagpole FP has two stay wires to the ground at A and B. They cannot be equidistant from P, as the ground is uneven. AB is 22m, ∠PAB is 34° and ∠PBA is 50°. Calculate the distances:
a) PA
b) PB.
If the angles of elevation of F from A is 49°, calculate:
c) FA
d) PF.

Q11 An aircraft leaves A and flies 257 km to B on a bearing of 257°. It then flies on to C, 215 km away on a bearing of 163° from B. Calculate:
a) ∠ABC
b) distance CA
c) the bearing needed to fly from A direct to C.

Q12 Mary and Jane were standing one behind the other, each flying a kite with two strings. The angles of elevation of the kite from the girls were 65° and 48° respectively. If Jane was 2.3 m behind Mary, calculate the length of each string.

SECTION THREE — BITS AND BOBS

3.9 Questions on the Graphs of Sin, Cos and Tan

Remember — Sin and Cos only have values between -1 and 1.

Q1

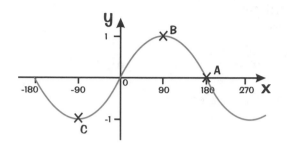

This is the graph of y = sin(x).
Write down the coordinates of the points A, B and C.

Q2

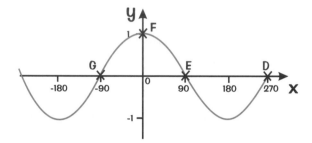

This is the graph of y = cos(x).
Write down the coordinates of the points D, E and F and G.

Q3   This is the graph of y = tan(x).
Write down the coordinates of the points h, i, and j.

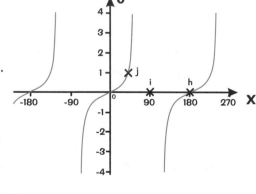

*Don't forget — something strange happens
with Tan at 90°, 270°, 450° etc. — it shoots off
to + infinity... still, at least it comes back again
(even if it is at - infinity.)*

Q4   Which of the graphs, y = sin(x),
y = cos (x), y = tan(x) go through
the points labelled A, B, C, ...J?
(Sometimes it is more than one).

Q5   Plot the points given in this table.

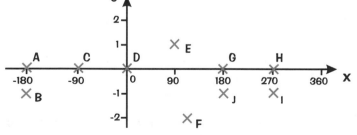

x	0	90	180	270	360
y	2	1	0	1	2

Write down an equation for the curve you have plotted.

Q6   Draw the curve of:
a) y = sin(2x)
b) y = 2sin(2x) for 0° ≤ x ≤ 360°.

Q7   Draw the curve of y = 1 + cos(x) for −180° ≤ x ≤ 180°

3.9 Questions on the Graphs of Sin, Cos and Tan

Q8 Draw the curve of y = – sin(x) for 0° ≤ x ≤ 360°.
What transformation is this of y = sin(x)?

Q9 Draw accurately the graph of y = 10cos(x) for –180° ≤ x ≤ 180°.
On the same axes draw the graph of 10y = x + 20.
Write down the coordinates of where the graphs cross. Show that this can be used to find a solution to the equation:

$$20 = 100\cos(x) - x.$$

Q10 Complete this table of values for sin(x) and (sin(x))².

X	0	10	20	30	40	50	60	70	80	90
sin x		0.17		0.5						1
(sin x)²		0.03		0.25						1

Draw axes for the graph from –180° ≤ x ≤ 180°.
Plot the points for (sin(x))².
From your knowledge of sin graphs, draw the rest of the graph for the limits given.

Q11 Draw accurately the graph of y = tan(x) for 0° ≤ x ≤ 360°. Let the y-axis have values –10 to +10.
On the same axis, draw the graph of 10y – x = 25.
Use your graphs to find an approximate solution to the equation x = 10tan(x) – 25.

Q12 Draw a table of points to plot y = tan(x) + sin(x):
a) for -90° ≤ x ≤ 90°

x	-90	-70	-50	-30	-10	0	10	30	50	70	90
tan x		-2.75			-0.18			0.58			
sin x		-0.94			-0.17			0.5			
y		-3.69			-0.35			1.08			

b) for 90° ≤ x ≤ 270°.

x	90	110	130	150	180	200	220	240	270
tan x			-1.19						
sin x			0.77						
y			-0.42						

Sketch the shape of the graph for –90° ≤ x ≤ 270.
Why did you need to plot such a wide range of points?

3.10   Questions on Angles of Any Size

Q1

Graph of y = sin x   −720 ⩽ x ⩽ 720

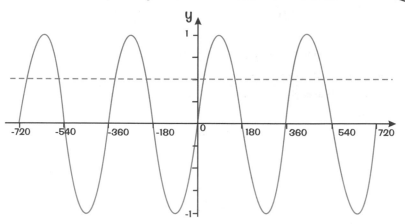

The dotted line drawn at y = 0.5 gives values of x as:
−690°, −570°, −330°, −210°, 30°, 150°, 390°, 510°.

Write down all the values of x between −720° and +720°, when:

a) sin(x) = −0.5

b) sin(x) = 0.1

c) sin(x) = −0.9.

Remember — the __Cos__ graph is __symmetrical__ about the line __x = 0__, but the __Sin__ graph __isn't__ — it might seem obvious now, but you can guarantee it won't in the Exam.

Q2   The graph of y = cos(x) is shown below for −720° ⩽ x ⩽ 720°.

Graph of y = cos x   −720 ⩽ x ⩽ 720

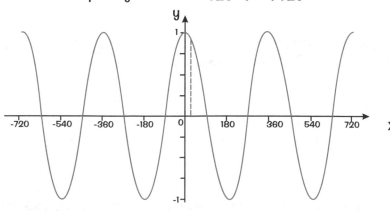

The dotted line drawn at x = 30° shows cos(30°) = 0.9.
Write down all the other angles between −720° and +720° when:

a) cos(x) = 0.9

b) cos(x) = 0.5

c) cos(x) = −0.6.

Explain why the positive and negative values are the same for cos, but not for sin.

3.10 Questions on Angles of Any Size

Q3 The graph of y = tan(x) is shown below for −450° ⩽ x ⩽ 450°.

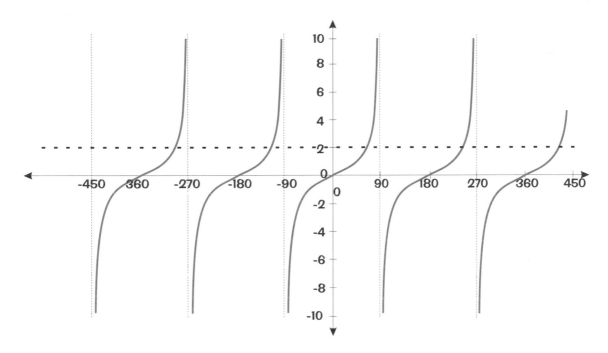

The dotted line drawn where y = 2 gives the values of x as:
−297°, −117°, 63°, 243°, 423°.

Write down all the values of x between −450° ⩽ x ⩽ 450° to the nearest degree when:
a) tan(x) = −1
b) tan(x) = 0.5
c) tan(x) = 3.

Q4 Write down 4 possible values of x, to the nearest degree, if:
a) sin(x) = 0.39
b) cos(x) = 0.39
c) tan(x) = −39.

Q5 Write down the sine, cosine and tangent of each of these angles to 3 s.f.
a) 175°
b) −175°
c) 405°
d) −735°.
e) What do you notice about the answers to a) and b)?
f) Can you explain what you notice?

3.11   Questions on Vectors

The Four Notations — weren't they a... no, never mind. You've got to know all of these,
so you can spot vectors a mile off and prepare yourself for the worst...

Q1   Write down the vectors lettered, then calculate the resultant vector. Check the
resultant from the diagram.

e.g.

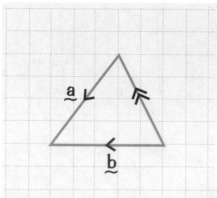

$$a = \begin{pmatrix} -3 \\ -4 \end{pmatrix} \qquad b = \begin{pmatrix} -5 \\ 0 \end{pmatrix}$$

$$-a + b = \begin{pmatrix} 3 \\ 4 \end{pmatrix} + \begin{pmatrix} -5 \\ 0 \end{pmatrix} = \begin{pmatrix} -2 \\ 4 \end{pmatrix}$$

as in the triangle.

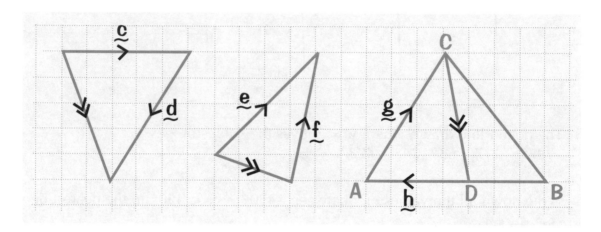

Q2 $p = \begin{pmatrix} 2 \\ 3 \end{pmatrix}$, $q = \begin{pmatrix} 0 \\ -2 \end{pmatrix}$, $r = \begin{pmatrix} 3 \\ -1 \end{pmatrix}$, $s = \begin{pmatrix} -1 \\ -2 \end{pmatrix}$

Calculate then draw:

a) p + q   **c)** 2r   **e)** 2p - 2s   **g)** 2r − q   **i)** p + 2s
b) p − q   **d)** s + p   **f)** 3q + s   **h)** ½q + 2r   **j)** q − 2r

Q3   M is the midpoint of $\overrightarrow{WX}$
$a = \overrightarrow{WZ}$ and $b = \overrightarrow{WM}$

If $\overrightarrow{MY} = c$, express in terms of a, b and c,

a) $\overrightarrow{MZ}$ **b)** $\overrightarrow{MX}$ **c)** $\overrightarrow{ZX}$ **d)** $\overrightarrow{XY}$ **e)** $\overrightarrow{ZY}$ **f)** $\overrightarrow{WY}$

3.11   *Questions on Vectors*

Q4   ABCDE is a pentagon.

$$\overrightarrow{AB} = \begin{pmatrix} 3 \\ 3 \end{pmatrix} \qquad \overrightarrow{AC} = \begin{pmatrix} 2 \\ 6 \end{pmatrix} \qquad \overrightarrow{AD} = \begin{pmatrix} -2 \\ 6 \end{pmatrix} \qquad \overrightarrow{AE} = \begin{pmatrix} -3 \\ 2 \end{pmatrix}$$

     a) Draw this pentagon accurately.

     b) Write down the vectors:

        i) $\overrightarrow{DE}$ **ii)** $\overrightarrow{DC}$ **iii)** $\overrightarrow{EC}$

     c) What sort of triangle is $\triangle$ACD?

Q5

$$\overrightarrow{OX} = 3\underset{\sim}{a} + 3\underset{\sim}{b}$$
$$\overrightarrow{OY} = 5\underset{\sim}{a} + 2\underset{\sim}{b}$$
$$\overrightarrow{OZ} = 6\underset{\sim}{a}$$

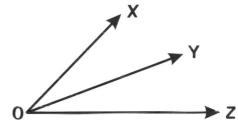

This diagram is not drawn to scale

Express in terms of a and b:

     a) $\overrightarrow{XY}$ **c)** $\overrightarrow{XZ}$

     b) $\overrightarrow{YZ}$ **d)** What does this tell you about triangle OXZ?

Q6

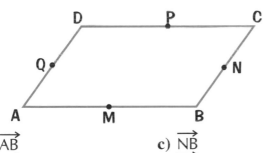

ABCD is a parallelogram.

MNPQ are mid points of the sides, as shown.
If $\overrightarrow{MQ} = \underset{\sim}{x}$ and $\overrightarrow{AM} = \underset{\sim}{y}$

Express in terms of $\underset{\sim}{x}$ and $\underset{\sim}{y}$:

     a) $\overrightarrow{AB}$ **c)** $\overrightarrow{NB}$ **e)** $\overrightarrow{AC}$

     b) $\overrightarrow{AQ}$ **d)** $\overrightarrow{BC}$ **f)** $\overrightarrow{BD}$

Q7   In the diagram on the right, EB and AC are perpendicular. ABCE is a parallelogram.
         $\angle$EDC is a right angle.

Name a vector equal to:

     a) $\overrightarrow{FC}$ **c)** $\overrightarrow{BC}$ **e)** $2\overrightarrow{CD}$ **g)** $\overrightarrow{EF} - \overrightarrow{CF}$

     b) $\overrightarrow{FB}$ **d)** $\overrightarrow{CE}$ **f)** $\overrightarrow{AE} + \overrightarrow{EC}$ **h)** $\overrightarrow{ED} + \overrightarrow{DC} + \overrightarrow{CB}$

     If AC = 16 cm and EB = 6 cm
     i) What is the area of ABCE?
     ii) What is the area of ABCDE?

Yep, you're gonna get to practise all that right angled triangle stuff — Pythagoras, Trig, that sort of thing.

Oh, how the winter evenings will just fly by.

3.12 Questions on Real Life Vectors

Look at the pretty pictures... make sure you can see how this little lot fit with the questions, because you'll have to draw your own on the next page.

Q1 In still water my motor boat can achieve 9 km/hr. I aim the boat directly across the river which is running at 3 km/hr. What is my resultant speed?

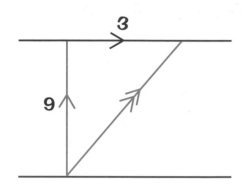

Q2

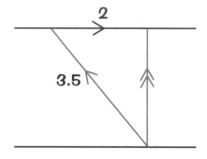

A girl wants to swim across a river running at 2 km/hr. If she can swim at 3.5 km/hr, calculate:

a) at what angle to the bank she should swim to go directly across

b) her resultant speed.

Q3 An aircraft is attempting to fly due North. It can achieve 600km/hr but there is a wind from the west at 75 km/hr. Calculate:

a) the actual bearing the aircraft is flying on

b) its resultant speed.

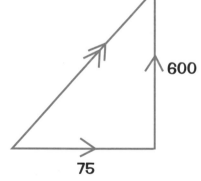

Q4 In the following diagrams the forces are acting on an object as shown.

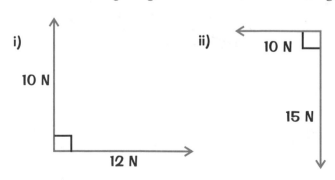

i) 10 N, 12 N

ii) 10 N, 15 N

iii) 23N, 20N

For each find:

a) the resultant force

b) its direction in relation to the larger force.

3.12   Questions on Real Life Vectors

For this next one, you've either got to <u>split the vectors into components</u> — F COS θ and F SIN θ, or just <u>add the vectors</u> together <u>end to end</u> and use the <u>Sine and Cosine rules</u>.

It's your call.

Q5   Two tugs are pulling a cruise ship with forces and directions as shown in the diagram. Find the forward resultant force.

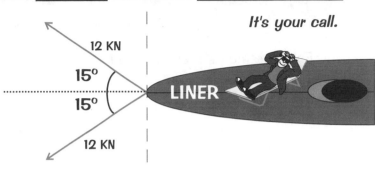

12 KN
15°
15°
LINER
12 KN

Q6   A helicoper can fly at 80 km/hr in still air. It takes off and heads North West but is blown off course by a North-Easterly wind of 30 km/hr.

  a) What is its resultant speed?

  b) If this helicopter wants to fly NW, on what bearing should it head?

Q7   A rowing boat needs to reach a point on the opposite bank directly across from its starting point. It can achieve a speed of 5 m/s in still water but the river runs at 2.5 m/s. Find the angle with the bank it must make if it is to achieve its objective.

Q8   Two cranes are lifting a bridge girder into place. They exert forces of 65 kN and 75 kN at 24° and 21° to the vertical, respectively. What is the resultant upward force?

Q9   A river is 16m wide. A boy who can swim at 2.4 km/hr in still water starts from A, to swim across the river which is running at 1.8 km/hr. Calculate:

  a) his resultant speed

  b) the direction he swims in relation to the bank

  c) how far downstream he lands

  d) how long it takes him.

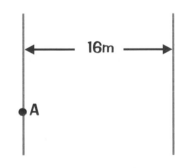

16m

A

Q10   A Christmas tree is suspended in front of a building by two wires at 45° and 35° to the horizontal. If the tensions in the wires are equivalent to a force of 50 N vertically, find S and T.

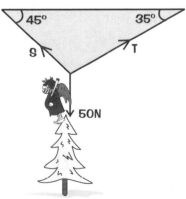

45°   35°
S   T
50N

Q11   A sailing boat can achieve 12 km/hr in still water. There is a current running due North at 4 km/hr. The boat wishes to sail North East. Calculate:

  a) the bearing it should set to achieve this

  b) the resultant speed obtained.

Q12   An aircraft is flying on a course of 290° at 350 km/hr. The wind is blowing and the aircraft actually flies on a bearing of 305° at 400 km/hr. Calculate the speed and direction of the wind.

4.1 Questions on Mean, Median, Mode, Range

For the mode and median, just identify the most frequent value and the middle value — easy.

The mean involves a bit more calculation, but hey, you are doing maths.

Q1   Find the mean, median, mode and range of these numbers:

1	2	–2	0	1	8	3	–3	2	4	–2	2

Q2   A village contains 4 households with no pets, 7 households with 1 pet, 5 households with 2 pets and 4 households with 3 pets. Find the mode, median and mean of the number of pets per household.

Q3   For the following 2 cases, which average would be most appropriate to use as a representative of the set of values:
a) men's shoe sizes in Hampshire
b) the numbers 8, 8.4, 8.9, 9.3, 9.7, 9.9, 10.1, 10.2, 1465?

Q4   A small company has 9 employees. Their salaries are as follows:

£13,000	£9,000	£7,500
£18,000	£12,000	£7,500
£23,000	£15,000	£11,500

a) Find the mean, median and mode of their salaries.
b) Which one does not give a good indication of their average salary?

Q5

1.2	3	–1.6	4.9	5.2	–2.4	7.4	5.2	–3	2.4

Using the above numbers find:
a) the mean
b) the mode
c) the median
d) the range.

Q6   The mean daily weight of potatoes sold in a greengrocers from Monday to Friday was 14 kg. The mean daily weight of potatoes sold from Monday to Saturday was 15 kg. How many kg of potatoes were sold on Saturday?

Q7   The average weight of the 11 players in a football team was 72.5 kg. The average weight of the 5 reserve players was 75.6 kg. What was the average weight of the whole squad? (Give your answer to 3 s.f.)

4.1 Questions on Mean, Median, Mode, Range

Don't forget, put the data in <u>ascending order</u> before looking for the averages.

Q8 Colonel Parsnips enters his village's prize marrow competition every year. Over the last 7 years the average weight of his entry was 4.2 kg. This year his average (now over 8 years) is 4.4 kg. Will the Colonel's entry outweigh Major Onions' 5.5 kg marrow?

Q9 A darts player scored 190 with 6 darts, the individual scores being as follows:

Darts 1 — treble 19
Darts 2 — treble 3
Darts 3 — treble 18
Darts 4 — single 20
Darts 5 — single 18
Darts 6 — double 16.

What is the mean score per dart?
(To the nearest whole number)

Q10 A travelling sales person covers the following distances during a week:

	Mon	Tue	Wed	Thur	Fri
Distance travelled (miles)	60	72	48	54	86

Calculate the mean number of miles travelled per day.

Q11 Over a 3 week period, Molly kept a record of how many minutes her school bus was either early or late. (She used + for late and - for early.)

+2	–1	0	+5	–4	–7	0
–8	0	+4	–4	–3	+14	+2

a) Calculate the mean lateness/earliness of the bus.
b) Calculate the median.
c) What is the mode?
d) The bus company use the answers to a), b) and c) to claim they are always on time, is this true?

Q12 The local rugby team scored the following number of tries in their first 10 matches of the season:

3	5	4	2	0	1	3	0	3	4

Find their modal number of tries.

4.1 Questions on Mean, Median, Mode, Range

 In these questions, you only need to look at the numbers and work out the averages. There's loads of stuff in here that you really don't need, so ignore it.

Q13 Colin averaged 83% over 3 exams. His average for the first two exams was 76%. What was Colin's score in the final exam?

Q14 At midday on the first day of every month of a year, the temperatures in Sheffield were recorded as:

> 2°C   –3°C   –1°C   2°C   5°C   9°C
>
> –2°C   15°C   18°C   18°C   7°C   12°C

What is the mean, median, mode and range of these temperatures?

Q15 The range for a certain list of numbers is 26, one of the numbers in the list is 48.
a) What is the lowest possible value a number in the list could be?
b) What is the highest possible value that could be in the list?

Q16 The bar graph shows the amount of time Jim and Bob spend watching TV during the week.

a) Find the mean amount of time per day each spends watching TV.

b) Find the range of times for each of them.

c) Using these values, comment on what you notice.

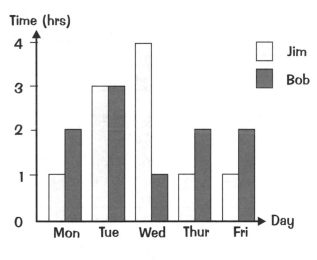

Q17 In each of the following cases, decide which average is referred to:
a) this average is least appropriate when the total number of values is small
b) this average is least affected if one of the values is chosen at random
c) this average is most affected by the presence of extreme values.

Q18 An ordinary dice is rolled 6 times, landing on a different number each time.
a) What is the mean score?
b) What is the median score?
c) What is the range of scores?

4.1 Questions on Mean, Median, Mode, Range

Q19 Mr Jones posted 88 Christmas cards first class on Monday. His friends received them over the week: 40 on Tuesday, 28 on Wednesday, 9 on Thursday, 6 on Friday and the remainder on Saturday.

a) Find the modal number of days it took for the cards to arrive.

b) Find the median number of days it took for the cards to arrive.

c) "The majority of first class post arrives within 2 days." Is the above statement true or false in the light of the data?

Q20 The pictogram shows the number of vehicles going over a bridge on each day of a week.

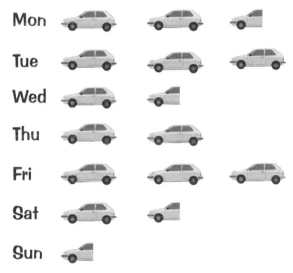

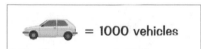 = 1000 vehicles

a) Calculate the mean number of vehicles going over the bridge each day.

b) What is the range of the number of vehicles?

Q21 An express courier van has a particular route throughout the week. The driver travels:

180 km on Monday
200 km on Tuesday
160 km on Wednesday
190 km on Thursday
90 km on Friday

Calculate the <u>mean number of kilometres</u> she travels per day.

If you've learnt anything about temperatures up north, the postal service or traffic volumes you've missed my point.

4.2 Questions on Probability

Q1 Charlton's cricket team had the following results over their last 20 matches.

W	W	L	D	D	W	W	L	W	L
D	L	L	D	W	D	W	W	L	L

a) Complete the frequency table.

b) Charlton reasons that since there are 3 possible results for any match, the probability that the next match will be drawn (D) is $\frac{1}{3}$. Explain why Charlton is wrong.

Outcome	Frequency
W	
D	
L	

c) Suggest a value for the probability of a draw based on the past performance of Charlton's team.

Q2 a) What is the probability of randomly selecting either a black Ace or black King from an ordinary pack of playing cards?

b) If the entire suit of clubs is removed from a pack of cards, what is the probability of randomly selecting a red 7?

c) If all the 7's are also removed from the pack of cards, what is the probability of randomly selecting the 4 of diamonds?

Q3 For the roulette wheel, the probability of the ball landing on each of the numbers is shown in the table below.

Number	1	2	3	4	5	6
Probability	$\frac{1}{6}$	$\frac{1}{3}$	$\frac{1}{6}$	$\frac{1}{12}$	$\frac{1}{12}$	$\frac{1}{6}$

a) Find the probability of landing on an even number.

b) What is the probability of landing on black?

c) Why is the probability of landing on a white or a 3 not $\frac{5}{12} + \frac{1}{6}$?

*Always start with a tree diagram — make sure you've learnt **everything** about them, then you can do **any** probability question... I promise.*

4.2   *Questions on Probability*

The __AND / OR Rules__ can get quite confusing, so get them drummed into that funny looking thing just between your neck and your hat __before__ the Exam...

For AND, you MULTIPLY (along the branches)
For OR, you ADD (the end results)

See — told you it was confusing.

Q4 There are 2 spinners: one with 3 sides numbered 1, 2, 3 the other with 7 sides numbered 1, 2, 3, 4, 5, 6, 7.

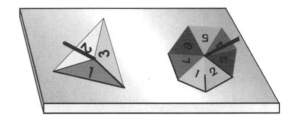

a) If both are spun together, list all the possible outcomes.

b) Complete the following table showing the sum of the 2 numbers for each outcome.

	1	2	3	4	5	6	7
1							
2							
3							

c) What is the probability that the sum is 6?
d) What is the probability that the sum is even?
e) What is the probability that the sum is greater than or equal to 8?
f) What is the probability that the sum is less than 8?
g) Explain how you can work out the probability in part **f)** without using the table.

Q5 There are 10 balls in a bag. 8 of the balls are white, 2 are black. Balls are selected at random from the bag, without replacement, until a black ball is obtained.

By extending the tree diagram below, or otherwise, calculate the probability that a black ball is selected on one of the first 3 goes.

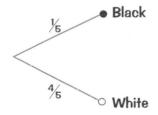

4.2 *Questions on Probability*

Q6 An unbiased dice in the shape of a tetrahedron has faces numbered 1, 2, 3, 4. To win a game with this dice, you must throw a 4. At each go you have a maximum of 3 attempts.

    a) Using a tree diagram, calculate the probability of winning with the second throw of the first go.

    b) What is the probability of winning on the first go?

Q7 3 balls are drawn at random, without replacement, from a bag containing 4 green balls and 3 red balls.

    a) Complete the tree diagram below showing all the possible outcomes and their probabilities.

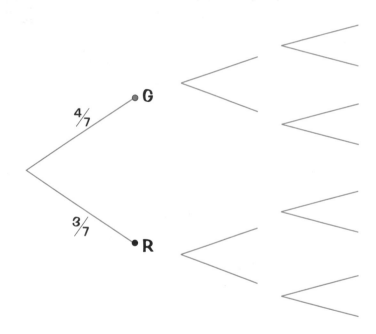

    b) What is the probability that exactly 2 green balls are drawn?

    c) What is the probability that the last ball drawn is the same colour as the first?

Q8 The notepad below shows orders for 4 different sorts of rice at a certain Indian restaurant. Based on this data, what is the probability that the next order of rice is:

    a) for pilau rice?

    b) for spicy mushroom or special fried rice?

    c) not for boiled rice?

boiled	20
pilau	24
spicy mushroom	10
special fried	6

They're getting easier already, aren't they...

4.2 Questions on Probability

Don't forget the "at least" trick — if you're looking for P(at least ...) happening, all you need to do is find 1 - P(not ...). If you do it the other way round it'll take ages, believe me.

Q9 How many times must you roll an ordinary 6 sided dice for the probability of getting at least one 6 to be more than 0.5?

Q10 In a 200 m swimming race between 8 boys, the probability of John winning the race if he is in one of the two outside lanes is $\frac{1}{4}$. If he is in any of the other lanes, the probability of John winning is $\frac{1}{3}$. If the lanes are drawn at random, what is the overall probability of John winning the race?

Q11 3 coins are drawn at random, without replacement, from a piggy bank containing 7 pound coins and 4 twenty pence pieces.
  a) Draw a tree diagram showing all possible outcomes and their probabilities.
  b) Find the probability that the first coin selected is different in value from the third.
  c) Find the probability that less than £1.50 is drawn altogether.

Q12 Trevor and his 2 brothers and 5 friends are seated at random in a row of seats at the cinema. What is the probability that Trevor has one brother on his immediate left and one on his immediate right?

Q13 Fabrizio is practising taking penalties. The probability that he misses the goal completely is $\frac{1}{8}$. The probability that the goal keeper saves the penalty is $\frac{3}{8}$. The probability that he scores is $\frac{1}{2}$. Fabrizio takes two penalties.

  a) Calculate the probability that Fabrizio fails to score with his two penalties.
  b) Calculate the probability that he scores only one goal.
  c) Calculate the probability that Fabrizio scores on neither or both of his 2 attempts.

4.3 Questions on Frequency Tables

Q1 130 female bus drivers were weighed to the nearest kg.
Calculate:
a) the median weight
b) the modal weight
c) the mean weight, by
first completing the table.

Weight (kg)	Frequency	Weight × Frequency
51	40	
52	30	
53	45	
54	10	
55	5	

You've got to be able to do these in both row and column form, because they could give you either one. There's no real difference, and the rules are still the same.

Q2 A travel company logs all calls to their sales desk. The number of calls per day received by the sales desk over a given year are shown below.

No. of Calls	10	11	12	13	14	15	16 and over
No. of Days	110	70	120	27	18	12	8

a) Find the median number of calls.
b) Find the modal number of calls.

Q3 20 pupils are asked to estimate the length (to the nearest m) of their gardens. Put the estimates in the frequency table below.

10, 8, 6, 4, 10, 8, 0, 14, 12, 8, 10, 6, 1, 6, 10, 8, 6, 6, 8, 8

a) Find the mode of the data.
b) Find the median of the data.
c) State the range of the data.

Length (m)	4 and under	6	8	10	12	14 and over
Frequency						

Q4 Using the computerised till in a shoe shop, the manager can predict what stock to order from the previous week's sales.
Opposite is the tabularised print-out for last week for men's shoes.

Shoe size	5	6	7	8	9	10	11
frequency	9	28	56	70	56	28	9

a) The mean, mode and median for this data can be compared. For each of the following statements decide whether it is true or false.
i) The <u>mode</u> for this data is <u>70</u>.
ii) The <u>mean</u> is <u>greater than</u> the <u>median</u> for this distribution.
iii) The mean, median and mode are <u>all equal</u> in this distribution.

b) What <u>percentage</u> of customers bought shoes of the <u>mean size</u> from last weeks sales data:

i) 30%　　　ii) 70%　　　iii) 0.273%　　or　　iv) 27.3%?

4.3 Questions on Frequency Tables

Don't forget to add the extra row or column.

Q5 A student has classes in Mathematics (M), English (E), French (F), Art (A) and Science (S).
Her timetable is:

Monday	S S E E A
Tuesday	E M M A A
Wednesday	S M E F F
Thursday	F E E A S
Friday	M M E S S

a) Complete the following frequency table for a weeks lessons:

b) Calculate the number of French lessons that the student will attend during a 12 week term.

c) What is the modal lesson?

Subject	M	E	F	A	S
Frequency					

Q6 A survey is carried out in a small village to find out how many bedrooms the houses have. The frequency table displays the results.

No. of bedrooms	1	2	3	4	5
Frequency	3	5	6	2	4

Find the mean, mode and median of the data.

Q7 A tornado has struck the hamlet of Moose-on-the-Wold. Many houses have had windows broken. The frequency table shows the devastating effects.

No. of windows broken per house	0	1	2	3	4	5	6
Frequency	5	3	4	11	13	7	2

a) Calculate the modal number of broken windows.

b) Calculate the median number of broken windows.

c) Calculate the mean number of broken windows.

4.4   Questions on Grouped Frequency

There are 3 tricky bits here: Class Boundaries, Mid-Interval Values and "How to Estimate the Mean" — make sure you __know all about them__ — because believe me, you need to.

Q1 The following sets of data are either continuous or can take distinct values only. In each case state which type of data is referred to.
   a) Hat sizes.
   b) Volumes of buckets.
   c) Weights of cheese bought in a supermarket.
   d) Lengths of bristles in a toothbrush.
   e) Total scores when 3 dice are rolled.
   f) Times taken to run 400 m.
   g) Populations of towns.

Q2 The times taken by Joseph to cycle to school each day are:

Time (mins)	Frequency
$16 \leqslant t < 18$	4
$18 \leqslant t < 20$	8
$20 \leqslant t < 22$	12
$22 \leqslant t < 24$	6

   a) On how many days did Joseph take 18 minutes or longer to cycle to school?
   b) How often did Joseph take less than 22 minutes?
   c) On how many days did Joseph record his times?

Q3 20 golfers achieved the following scores during a round of golf:
   67, 62, 72, 78, 68, 69, 60, 84, 71, 63, 78, 71, 65, 69, 75, 80, 72, 66, 74, 66.

   a) Complete the following table:

Score	Tally	Frequency
$59.5 \leqslant s < 64.5$		
$64.5 \leqslant s < 69.5$		
$69.5 \leqslant s < 74.5$		
$74.5 \leqslant s < 84.5$		

   b) How many golfers scored less than 74.5?
   c) How many golfers scored at least 69.5?
   d) Explain why it is not possible to determine the number of golfers who scored less than 73 using the table alone?

4.4 Questions on Grouped Frequency

Q4 The weights of 18 newly felled trees are noted below:

272.7	333.2	251.0	200.2	246.5	312.8	256.1	398.0
344.3	226.8	362.0	348.3	232.9	309.7	284.5	327.4
328.0	259.6						

a) Complete the frequency table.

Weight (kg)	Tally	Frequency	Mid-Interval	Frequency × Mid-Interval
200 – 249				
250 – 299				
300 – 349				
350 – 399				

b) Estimate the mean weight using the frequency table.
c) What is the modal group?

Q5 The heights of all the trees in an orchard were measured and recorded:

4.2	4.7	3.7	3.1	4.4	3.6	4.6
4.1	3.7	3.05	4.8	4.2	3.6	3.45
4.6	4.2	3.65	3.7	4.05	4.32	

a) Put the data into the frequency table.

Height	3 – 3.49	3.5 – 3.99	4 – 4.49	4.5 – 4.99
Frequency				
Mid-Interval				
Frequency × Mid-Interval				

b) What is the modal group?
c) Estimate the mean using the frequency table.
d) Calculate the mean value using the original data.
e) Comment on your answers to parts **c)** and **d)**.

SECTION FOUR — STATISTICS

4.4   *Questions on Grouped Frequency*

Q1   Over the season, the school rugby team charted their scores using a tally on the table below.

Score	Tally	Frequency	Mid-Interval	Frequency × Mid-Interval
0 – 19	卌 I			
20 – 39	III			
40 – 59	卌 II			
60 – 79	II			
80 – 99	II			

a) Complete the frequency table.

b) What is the modal group?

c) Estimate the mean score.

d) Which group contains the median score?

Q2   On Johnny McGregor's farm, there are 16 turkeys ready for market. The weights of the turkeys, accurate to the nearest lb, are:

9	12	15	14	10	13	15	14
17	13	9	14	15	15	13	14

a) Complete the frequency table of turkey weights

Weight (lb)	Tally	Frequency	Mid-Interval	Frequency × Mid-Interval
8 – 9				
10 – 11				
12 – 13				
14 – 15				
16 – 17				

b) How many turkeys are in the 10 — 11 group?

c) What is the modal group?

d) Estimate the mean using the mid-interval technique, and compare this estimate with the mean calculated from the data.

Q3   The speeds of 32 skiers at a certain corner of a downhill course are tabulated below.

Speed (km/h)	40 – 44	45 – 49	50 – 54	55 – 59	60 – 64
Frequency	4	8	10	7	3
Mid-Interval					
Frequency × Mid-Interval					

a) By completing the frequency table, estimate the mean speed.

b) How many skiers were travelling at less than 54.5 km/h?

c) How many skiers were travelling more than 49.5 km/h?

4.4   *Questions on Grouped Frequency*

Remember, you can't find the __exact__ value of the median... but you __can__ say which group it's in. The method's just the same as before, apart from that.

Q4   The number of customers each evening at a certain Indian restaurant on 50 separate occasions were recorded:

63	43	61	55	28	60	17	89	83	11	75	49	64	55	57
80	85	41	78	45	58	87	51	70	91	71	29	77	65	80
69	48	72	51	24	58	53	76	52	52	8	64	36	19	96
66	23	44	80	20

No. of Customers					
Tally					
Frequency					
Mid-Interval					
Frequency × Mid-Interval					

a) Choosing suitable class intervals, reduce this data into a frequency table.

b) Estimate the mean number of customers and compare this estimate with the mean calculated from the raw data.

c) Construct a frequency polygon by plotting class frequency against mid-interval value.

Q5   48 numbers are recorded below:

0.057	0.805	0.056	0.979	0.419	0.160	0.534	0.763
0.642	0.569	0.773	0.055	0.349	0.892	0.664	0.136
0.528	0.792	0.085	0.546	0.549	0.908	0.639	0.000
0.614	0.478	0.421	0.472	0.292	0.579	0.542	0.356
0.070	0.890	0.883	0.333	0.033	0.323	0.544	0.668
0.094	0.049	0.049	0.999	0.632	0.700	0.983	0.356

a) Transfer the data into the frequency table.

Number	$0 \leqslant n < 0.2$	$0.2 \leqslant n < 0.4$	$0.4 \leqslant n < 0.6$	$0.6 \leqslant n < 0.8$	$0.8 \leqslant n < 1$
Tally					
Frequency					
Mid-Interval					
Frequency × Mid-Interval					

b) Which is the modal class?

c) Which group contains the median?

d) Estimate the mean value.

4.5   Questions on Cumulative Frequency

Ah, curves, that's more like it. From cumulative frequency curves you can find three lovely things with three lovely names...

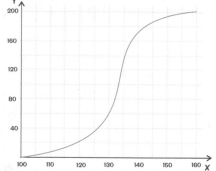

Q1   Using the cumulative frequency curve, read off the:

a) median

b) lower quartile

c) upper quartile

d) inter-quartile range.

Q2   The ages of all the people in a small village are contained in the frequency table.

Age	$0 \leqslant a < 20$	$20 \leqslant a < 40$	$40 \leqslant a < 60$	$60 \leqslant a < 80$	$80 \leqslant a < 100$
Frequency	9	37	44	16	4
Cumulative Frequency					

a) Complete the cumulative frequency table.

b) Plot a cumulative frequency curve.

c) From your graph read off the median value.

d) What is the interquartile range?

Q3   The number of passengers using a bus service each day, has been recorded over a 4 week period. The data is presented in the table below:

No. passengers	0 – 49	50 – 99	100 – 149	150 – 199	200 – 249	250 – 299
Frequency	2	7	10	5	3	1
Cumulative Frequency						
Mid-Interval						
Frequency × Mid-Interval						

A mean passenger

a) By completing the table, estimate the mean number of passengers.

b) By plotting a cumulative frequency curve, determine the median value.

c) What is the modal group?

Q4   40 pupils have taken an exam and their marks are recorded in a frequency table.

Mark (%)	$0 \leqslant m < 20$	$20 \leqslant m < 40$	$40 \leqslant m < 60$	$60 \leqslant m < 80$	$80 \leqslant m < 100$
Frequency	2	12	18	5	3
Cumulative Frequency					

a) Complete the table and plot the cumulative frequency curve.

b) What is the value of the lower quartile?

c) What is the interquartile range?

d) What is the median mark?

4.5   Questions on Cumulative Frequency

Some of these questions ask you to draw a box plot as well. Remember, it's much easier to put it directly under the cumulative frequency curve you've just drawn. Then you can extend the lines for the median and quartiles, rather than having to re-measure them.

Q5   A group of parents carried out a survey on the price of trainers, then tabulated the results.

a) Fill in the rest of the table.

b) How many trainers did the parents investigate?

c) Plot the cumulative frequency curve.

Prices of Trainers (£)	0 – 29	30 – 59	60 – 89	90 – 119	120 – 149	150 – 179
Frequency	4	18	24	20	11	3
Cumulative Frequency						
Mid-Interval						
Frequency × Mid-Interval						

d) Which is more expensive, the mean or the median price?

Q6   Billy noted down the approximate wingspans (cm) of birds in his garden during one weekend:

```
       33   23   31   33   37   42   27   42   36   34
       30   25   43   39   38   49   33   38   47   36
       21   31   28   34   31   36   30   39   32   33
```

a) Put the data into this frequency table.

Wing Span (cm)	20 – 24	25 – 29	30 – 34	35 – 39	40 – 44	45 – 49
Frequency						
Cumulative Frequency						
Mid-Interval						
Frequency × Mid-Interval						

b) Construct the cumulative frequency curve.

c) What is the value of the lower quartile?

d) What value does the upper quartile take?

e) Draw the box plot underneath the cumulative frequency curve.

f) Estimate the mean using the tabulated data, and compare this with the median wingspan.

Q7   The top 100 scores for a board game are presented in the table below.

Score	31 – 40	41 – 50	51 – 60	61 – 70	71 – 80	81 – 90	91 – 100
Frequency	4	12	21	32	19	8	4
Cumulative Frequency							

a) What is the modal group?

b) Which group contains the median score?

c) By plotting the cumulative frequency curve, determine the actual value of the median score.

d) Find the interquartile range.

e) Draw the box plot.

4.5 Questions on Cumulative Frequency

Q1 The frequency table contains the height of 86 pieces of bread dough which have been proved for 20 minutes.

Height (mm)	8 – 9	10 – 11	12 – 13	14 – 15	16 – 17	18 – 19	20 – 21	22 – 23
Frequency	2	9	21	26	17	8	2	1
Cumulative Frequency								
Mid-Interval								
Frequency × Mid-Interval								

a) By completing the table, estimate the mean height.

b) By drawing the cumulative frequency curve determine the median height.

c) Find the interquartile range.

Q2 The following frequency table gives the distribution of the lives of electric bulbs.

a) Complete the frequency table.

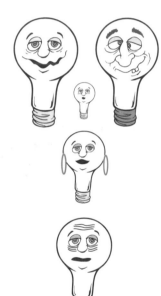

Life (hours)	Frequency	Cumulative Frequency	Mid-Interval
900 – 999	10		
1000 – 1099	12		
1100 – 1199	15		
1200 – 1299	18		
1300 – 1399	22		
1400 – 1499	17		
1500 – 1599	14		
1600 – 1699	9		

b) Which group contains the median value?

c) By drawing the cumulative frequency curve, find the actual value of the median.

d) Determine values for the upper and lower quartiles.

Yeah, I know these are a bit fiddly, but they're easy marks, so take your time and make sure you pick every last one up.

Q3 The populations of 50 villages are recorded in the table below:

Population	1 – 500	501 – 1000	1001 – 1500	1501 – 2000	2001 – 2500	2501 – 3000
Frequency	4	10	18	12	4	2
Cumulative Frequency						
Mid-Interval						

a) Which is the modal class?

b) Which group contains the median value?

c) Complete the table and draw the cumulative frequency curve.

d) Determine the median and the interquartile range.

SECTION FOUR — STATISTICS

4.5 Questions on Cumulative Frequency

Q5 The price (£) of the cars on Charlie's Cut Price Motors forecourt are:
299 499 162 296 269 352 127 249 234 193
209 396 257 35   201 301 179 212 134 211

a) Complete the frequency table.

Price (£)	0 – 100	101 – 200	201 – 300	301 – 400	401 – 500
Frequency					
Cumulative Frequency					
Mid-Interval					

b) How many cars are on the forecourt?

c) What is the total value of the cars?

d) By drawing a cumulative frequency curve determine the median and the upper and lower quartiles.

e) Draw the box plot underneath the cumulative frequency curve.

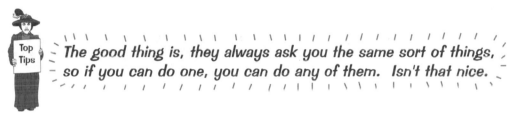

The good thing is, they always ask you the same sort of things, so if you can do one, you can do any of them. Isn't that nice.

Q6 30 pupils recorded the time taken (minutes : seconds) to boil some water,
2:37 2:37 3:17 3:30 2:45 2:13 3:18 3:12 3:38 3:29
3:04 3:24 4:13 3:01 3:11 2:33 3:37 4:24 3:59 3:11
3:22 3:13 2:57 3:12 3:07 4:17 3:31 3:42 3:51 3:24

a) By using a tally, transfer the data into the frequency table.

Time	$2:00 \leqslant t < 2:30$	$2:30 \leqslant t < 3:00$	$3:00 \leqslant t < 3:30$	$3:30 \leqslant t < 4:00$	$4:00 \leqslant t < 4:30$
Tally					
Frequency					
Cumulative Frequency					
Mid-Interval					

b) Draw the cumulative frequency curve.

c) Using your graph, read off the median and the upper and lower quartiles.

d) What is the interquartile range?

e) And draw the box plot under the cumulative frequency curve. Just for a laugh, like.

4.6 Questions on Scatter Graphs and Histograms

*A **SCATTER GRAPH** is just a load of points on a graph that end up in a bit of a mess, rather than in a nice line or curve. There's a fancy word to say how much of a mess they're in — it's **CORRELATION**.*

Q1 Match the following diagrams with the most appropriate descriptive label.

Labels: (P) Strong positive correlation   (S) Moderate negative correlation
 (Q) Exact negative correlation   (T) Medium correlation
 (R) Little or no correlation   (U) Exact positive correlation.

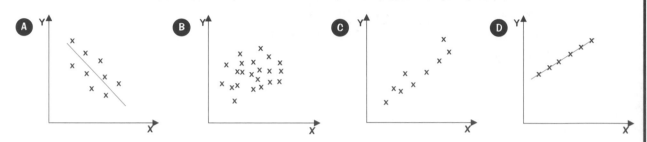

To draw a scatter graph, you just plot the points you're given on a graph.

Q2 10 people took 2 exams in Welding for Beginners. The table shows the marks obtained.

Candidate	1	2	3	4	5	6	7	8	9	10
Exam 1 (%)	85	30	55	10	40	20	0	95	65	40
Exam 2 (%)	70	25	50	15	70	25	5	80	60	35

a) Draw a scatter graph representing this information.

b) Draw a line of best fit.

c) Clive only sat the first exam, obtaining a mark of 50%. Use your scatter graph to estimate the mark that he might have achieved if he had sat the second exam.

Q3 A local electrical store has kept a log of the number of CD players sold at each price:

Price (£)	£80	£150	£230	£310	£380	£460
No. Sold	27	24	22	19	17	15

a) Draw this information as a scatter graph, using suitable axes.

b) Draw a line of best fit and use it to estimate:

 i) the number of CD players the shopkeeper could expect to sell for £280

 ii) the price to charge for a CD player which would sell to 20 people.

c) Is the data positively or negatively correlated?

CD player log

4.6 Questions on Scatter Graphs and Histograms

Q4 8 friends are comparing heights and shoe sizes to see if they are correlated. The data is tabulated below:

Height	4'6"	4'8"	5'2"	5'5"	5'8"	5'10"	6'	6'6"
Shoe size	4	5	4.5	5	6	8	9	12

a) Plot the points on a scatter graph.

b) Are the points positively or negatively correlated?

c) By fitting an appropriate line, estimate the shoe size of another friend who is 6'2".

Q5 The bowling and batting averages for the members of a village cricket team are given in the table.

a) Draw a scatter diagram for the above data.

b) State the type of correlation, if any.

Batting	8	13	17	26	29	35	37	40	45	52	57
Bowling	32	13	22	31	14	22	6	10	50	39	12

Q6 Janine is convinced that the more expensive cookery books contain more pages. To test out her theory, she has compiled the table:

Price	£4.25	£5.00	£4.75	£6.25	£7.50	£8.25	£4.75	£5.00	£6.75	£3.25	£3.75
No. of pages	172	202	118	184	278	328	158	138	268	84	98

a) Draw a scatter graph to represent this information.

b) Draw in a line of best fit.

c) Use your line to estimate the price of a book containing 250 pages.

It's the <u>size that counts</u>... You've got to look at the <u>area</u> of the bars, which means looking at the <u>width</u> as well as the height.

Q7 The histogram below represents the age distribution of people that watch outdoor bog snorkelling. Given that there are 24 people in the 40 – 55 age range, find the number of people in all the other age ranges.

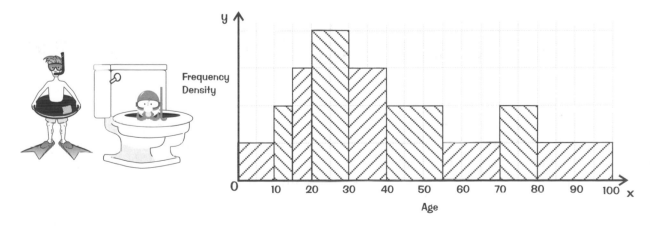

4.6 Questions on Scatter Graphs and Histograms

Top Tips: *The most important thing with your line of best fit is to make sure you've got as many points on one side of the line as you've got on the other. Don't worry if there aren't that many points right on it, they're supposed to be a bit messy.*

Q8 The examination results (%) for a group of students for 2 exams are shown in the table.

Physics	97	61	36	56	48	84	83	79	26	66
Chemistry	98	65	49	66	60	88	87	85	43	78

a) Represent the data with a scatter graph.
b) State the type of correlation, if any.

Q9 The heights of all the buildings on an industrial estate are recorded in a table:

Height (m)	0 – 3	4 – 6	7 – 10	11 – 15	16 – 25
Frequency	7	6	12	15	20
Frequency density					

a) Fill in the frequency density row.
b) Draw a histogram using this data.
c) Using your histogram, estimate the number of buildings which are less than 5m high.

Q10 The weight of honey collected from several beehives is tabulated below:

a) Complete the frequency table by calculating the frequency densities.
b) Draw a histogram to represent this data.
c) Use your histogram to estimate the number of bee hives producing more than 6 kg of honey.

Weight (kg)	0 – 2	3 – 4	5 – 7	8 – 9	10 – 15
Frequency	3	2	6	9	12
Frequency density					

Q11 The prices of Persian rugs available in a catalogue are:

Price (£)	$0 \leqslant P < 50$	$50 \leqslant P < 100$	$100 \leqslant P < 150$	$150 \leqslant P < 200$	$200 \leqslant P < 250$	$250 \leqslant P < 300$	$300 \leqslant P < 350$	$350 \leqslant P < 400$
Frequency	10	25	45	57	63	12	10	10
Frequency density								

a) State the modal class.
b) By first completing the table, draw a histogram to represent the data.
c) Estimate the number of rugs priced at less than £125.

98

SECTION FOUR — STATISTICS

4.6 Questions on Scatter Graphs and Histograms

Always use <u>area blocks</u> to find out how much each bar represents.
Check out P.54 of The Revision Guide for a few easy rules to learn. What fun.

Q12 The lifetimes of 96 microwaves are tabulated:

Lifetime (years)	$0 \leqslant L < 2$	$2 \leqslant L < 4$	$4 \leqslant L < 6$	$6 \leqslant L < 8$	$8 \leqslant L < 10$	$10 \leqslant L < 12$
Frequency	15	22	36	9	10	4
Frequency density						
Mid-Interval						
Frequency × Mid-Interval						

a) Complete the frequency table.
b) Estimate the mean lifetime.
c) Which group contains the median value?
d) How many lifetimes are outside the modal group?
e) Draw a histogram and use it to determine the number of microwaves with lifetimes shorter than 5 years.

Q13 On a particular day, the length of time people spent on a beach was recorded:

Length of time (mins)	0 — 5	6 — 10	11 — 20	21 — 40	41 — 80	81 — 100
Frequency	11	24	48	48	24	11
Frequency density						

a) Fill in the last row of the table.
b) Draw a histogram to represent this data.
c) How many people spent more than 8 minutes on the beach?

Q14 A group of sixth formers took part in a survey to see how much time they spent watching TV each week.

a) Complete the table by filling in the frequency density column.
b) How many students took part in the survey?
c) Represent the data as a histogram.
d) Estimate the number of students that watch more than 7, but less than 13 hours each week.

No. of hours	Frequency	Frequency density
0 – 1	6	
2 – 3	13	
4 – 5	15	
6 – 8	9	
9 – 10	23	
11 – 15	25	
16 – 20	12	

SECTION FOUR — STATISTICS

4.7 Questions on Histograms and Dispersion

 Know your shapes — they're bound to ask you what different shaped graphs mean.

Q1 Match the histograms to their corresponding cumulative frequency curves.

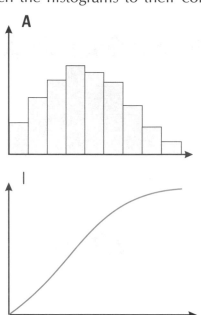

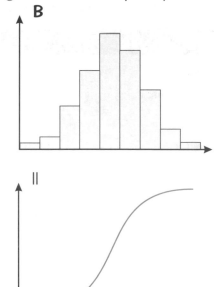

Q2 Draw two contrasting histograms showing the weights of a sample of eight year olds and the weights of a sample of 16 year olds.

Q3 Find the mean of the following data: 6, 2, -4, 5, -1, 7, -10, 11.

Q4 Find the mean of the following data sets.
  a) -2, -4, 4, 6, -10, 10
  b) 21, 23, 19, 22, 21, 23, 20, 22
  c) 579, 791, 3989, 184, 369
  d) 87, 42, 53, 35, 61, 36
  e) -56, -23, -93, -70, -22, -30
  f) $2^1, 2^2, 2^3, 2^4, 2^5$

Q5 The daily sales of petrol, in gallons, during a 2 week period for a petrol filling station that is open seven days a week, are as follows:

	Mon	Tue	Wed	Thur	Fri	Sat	Sun
Week 1	650	310	540	570	630	660	300
Week 2	550	310	490	560	540	680	340

Which is greater, the mean value for week 1 or for week 2?

4.7 Questions on Histograms and Dispersion

Q6 A farmer keeps track of the amount of milk produced by his cows each day.

Amount of Milk (Litres)	Frequency	Frequency Density	Mid-Interval	Frequency × Mid-Interval
$0 \leqslant C < 1$	6			
$1 \leqslant C < 5$	6			
$5 \leqslant C < 8$	6			
$8 \leqslant C < 10$	6			
$10 \leqslant C < 15$	6			
$15 \leqslant C < 20$	6			

a) Complete the frequency table.
b) Use the mid-interval technique to estimate the mean.
c) Draw a histogram to show the data.
d) On how many days is less than 8 litres produced?

Q7 Find the mean of the following data sets:
a) 20, 18, 16, 14, 12, 16, 0, 4, 6, 8
b) 8, 6, 6, 3, 2, 1, 5, 1, 2, 2, 4, 3, 3, 4, 3
c) 10, 9, 8, 8, 8, 8, 7, 7, 4, 3.

Q8 A magazine has carried out a survey to see how much pocket money its readers receive each week.

Amount (£)	Frequency	Frequency Density	Mid-Interval	Frequency × Mid-Interval
0 — 0.50	11			
0.60 — 0.90	25			
1.00 — 1.20	9			
1.30 — 1.40	12			
1.50 — 1.70	24			
1.80 — 2.40	21			
2.50 — 3.00	54			
3.10 — 4.00	32			

a) By first completing the table, estimate the mean amount of pocket money.
b) What is the modal class?
c) Draw a histogram to represent the data.
d) How many readers receive more than £1.35 each week?

4.8 Questions on Stem and Leaf Diagrams

A stem and leaf diagram is a bit like a histogram, except there's no axes. The information is in the form of raw data. Just read off the numbers.

Q1 List the values shown in this stem and leaf diagram in ascending order.

Just to start you off, the first five values are: 3, 3, 3, 5, 8

```
0 | 3 3 3 5 8 8 9
1 | 2 3 4 4 8 8 9
2 | 0 2 2 4
3 | 1 3
```
Key: 1 | 4 means 14

Q2 This stem and leaf diagram shows the marks in a test for a group of 25 students.

```
0  |
5  | 0 1
10 | 0 1 4
15 | 0 2 2 3 3 4
20 | 1 1 1 2 4 4
25 | 1 2 3 4
30 | 1 4 4
35 | 4
```
Key: 15 | 3 means 18

Use the information in the diagram to answer these questions:
a) Find the number of students scoring 18.
b) Find the number of students scoring 10-15 inclusive.
c) Find the number of students scoring 28 or more:
d) Find the highest score.
e) Find the modal score.
f) Find the mean score.
g) Find the median score.

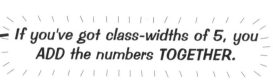
If you've got class-widths of 5, you ADD the numbers TOGETHER.

Q3 I did a survey to find out how many living relatives my friends have. Here are my results:

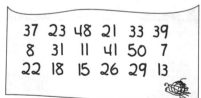
```
37 23 48 21 33 39
 8 31 11 41 50  7
22 18 15 26 29 13
```

Draw a stem and leaf diagram to represent this data. Use this key:

Key: 1 | 4 means 14

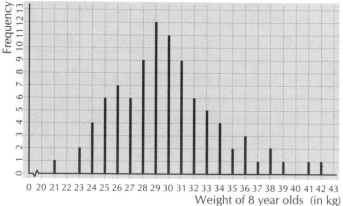

Q4 Use the information from this line graph to create your own stem and leaf diagram, using class-widths of 5. Then make a key to show how to use your diagram.

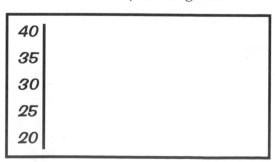
```
40 |
35 |
30 |
25 |
20 |
```
Key: | means

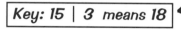
Frequency vs Weight of 8 year olds (in kg), 0 20 21 22 23 24 25 26 27 28 29 30 31 32 33 34 35 36 37 38 39 40 41 42 43

4.9 Questions on Time Series

Time Series — don't you just love 'em. These little horrors are pretty important, and could easily raise their ugly head in the Exam. Do yourself a favour and practise them.

Q1 Which of the following sets of measurements form time series?

a) The average rainfall in Cumbria, measured each day for a year.

b) The daily rainfall in European capital cities on Christmas Day, 2000.

c) The shoe size of everybody in Class 6C on September 1st, 2001.

d) My shoe size (measured every month) from when I was twelve months old to when I was fourteen years old.

Q2 a) Which two of the following time series are seasonal, and which two are not seasonal?

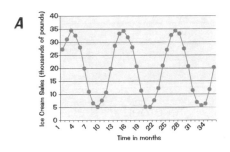

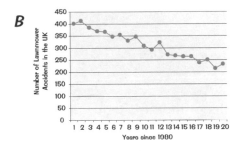

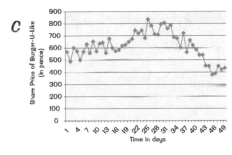

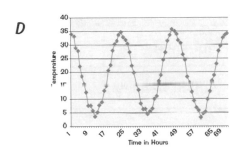

b) What are the periods of the time series which are seasonal?

c) Describe the trends in the time series which are **not** seasonal.

Q3 The following table shows the value of a knitwear company's sock sales in the years 1998-2000. The sales figures are given in thousands of pounds.

Time	Sales
Spring 1998	404
Summer 1998	401
Autumn 1998	411
Winter 1998	420
Spring 1999	416
Summer 1999	409
Autumn 1999	419
Winter 1999	424
Spring 2000	416
Summer 2000	413
Autumn 2000	427
Winter 2000	440

a) Plot the figures on a graph with time on the horizontal axis and sales on the vertical axis.

b) Calculate a 4-point moving average to smooth the series. Write your answers in the boxes provided.

c) Plot the moving average on the same axes as your original graph.

d) Describe the trend of the sales figures.

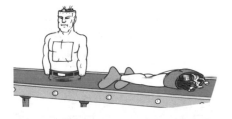

4.10   Questions on Frequency (Mixed)

This is just a bit more practice at what you've been doing for the last few pages, really.

Q1   100 domestic dogs were weighed to the nearest kg.
Find:
a) the median weight
b) the mode
c) the mean, by first completing the table.

Weight (kg)	Frequency	Weight × Frequency
15	35	
16	20	
17	25	
18	20	

Q2   The lengths of the girls' hair, in a particular school, is recorded in the table below:

Length (cm)	0 — 5	6 — 10	11 — 15	16 — 25	26 — 50
Frequency	22	27	31	54	35
Frequency density					

a) Which is the modal class?
b) How many of the girls are outside the modal class?
c) Draw a histogram showing this data.
d) Estimate the number of girls whose hair is less than 8 cm in length.

Q3   Two rival newsagents have recorded their sales of the local newspaper every day for one week:

	Mon	Tue	Wed	Thur	Fri	Sat	Sun
Newsagent 1	10	15	50	30	18	40	29
Newsagent 2	5	25	35	17	28	30	16

By calculating the mean number of newspapers sold by each newsagent, determine which newsagent, on average, sells the most each day.

4.10 Questions on Frequency (Mixed)

Q4 A school organised a sponsored walk to raise funds. To keep track of the distances walked by each of the 100 walkers, the head teacher compiled a frequency table.

Distance (miles)	$0 \leqslant d < 3$	$3 \leqslant d < 6$	$6 \leqslant d < 9$	$9 \leqslant d < 12$	$12 \leqslant d < 15$
Frequency	3	6	10	27	54
Mid-Interval					
Frequency × Mid-Interval					

a) Estimate the mean distance, by first completing the frequency table.

b) What is the maximum value for the range of distances?

Q5 On a particular day the rainfall at various sites across the UK was measured and tabulated.

Rainfall (mm)	0 – 2	3 – 5	6 – 8	9 – 11	12 – 14	15 – 17	18 – 20	21 – 23
Frequency	2	7	18	40	22	11	9	1
Cumulative Frequency								
Mid-Interval								
Frequency × Mid-Interval								

a) Complete the table and use it to plot the cumulative frequency curve.

b) Using the table estimate the mean value, and compare this with the median value obtained from the curve.

c) What is the interquartile range for the rainfall?

Q6 As part of a traffic control scheme, the speeds of cars on a certain stretch of road were recorded.

Speed (mph)	Frequency	Mid-Interval	Frequency × Mid-Interval
$29.5 < s < 34.5$	11		
$34.5 < s < 39.5$	21		
$39.5 < s < 44.5$	52		
$44.5 < s < 49.5$	43		
$49.5 < s < 54.5$	31		

a) Complete the frequency table and use this to estimate the mean speed.

b) What is the modal speed group?

c) Which group contains the median speed?

4.11 *Questions on Sampling Methods*

Q1 Give the definition of:
a) random sampling
b) systematic sampling
c) stratified sampling
d) quota sampling.

You've got to know the 4 main types of sampling — have a go at Q1, and if you can't get it right, keep trying 'till you can.

You've also got to be able to spot problems and criticise sampling techniques — basically, if you think it's a load of rubbish, you get the chance to say why.

Q2 Give a reason why the following methods of sampling are poor:
a) a survey carried out inside a newsagents concluded that 80% of the population buy a daily newspaper
b) a phone poll conducted at 11 am on a Sunday morning revealed that less than 2% of the population regularly go to church
c) 60% of the population were estimated to watch the 9 o' clock news each evening after a survey was carried out at a bridge club.

Q3 Decide which of the following questions (if any) are suitable for a survey to find which of five desserts (cheesecake, fruit salad, sherry trifle, knickerbocker glory and chocolate cake) people like the most. Give a reason for each of your answers.
a) Do you like cheesecake, fruit salad, sherry trifle, knickerbocker glory or chocolate cake?
b) How often do you eat dessert?
c) Which is your favourite out of: cheesecake; fruit salad; sherry trifle; knickerbocker glory; chocolate cake.
d) What is your favourite dessert?
e) Is your favourite dessert: cheesecake; fruit salad; sherry trifle; knickerbocker glory; chocolate cake; none of these.

Q4 A newspaper contained the following article regarding the amount of exercise teenagers take outside school.

a) Suggest 3 questions that you could use in a survey to find out whether this is true at your school.
b) At a particular school there are 300 pupils in each of years 7 to 11. There are approximately equal numbers of girls and boys. Describe how you would select 10% of the pupils for a stratified sample which is representative of all the pupils at the school.

Over half of all teenagers do no exercise at all. Only one in ten play team sports or take part in individual sports.
blah-blah-blah-blah-blah
blah-blah-blah-blah-blah
blah-blah-blah-blah-blah blah-blah-blah-blah-blah
blah-blah-blah-blah-blah blah-blah-blah-blah-blah
blah-blah-blah-blah-blah blah-blah-blah-blah-blah
blah-blah-blah-blah-blah blah-blah-blah-blah-blah
blah-blah-blah-blah-blah

4.11 Questions on Sampling Methods

Q5 Pauline is the manager of a small cafe. She knows that some of her customers buy cold drinks from the cold drinks machine, some buy hot drinks from the hot drinks machine and some people buy snacks and drinks at the counter.

Pauline would like to use a questionnaire to find out whether she should stock a new brand of cola. Here is part of Pauline's questionnaire:

Cafe Questionnaire

1) Please tick the box to show how often you visit the cafe:

daily ☐   weekly ☐   fortnightly ☐   monthly ☐   less than monthly ☐

a) Using the same style, design another question that Pauline can include in her questionnaire.

b) Pauline hands out her questionnaire as she serves customers at the counter. Give a reason why this is a suitable or unsuitable way to hand out the questionnaire.

Statistics Crossword

ACROSS

1) You can easily find the range and average from this type of table. (9)

5) A method of sampling which tries to use the same proportions as the whole population. (5)

7) The likelihood of you guessing this clue is conditional to whether you know 2, 3 and 6 down. (11)

8) It's not a matter of being cruel, its just a way of working out averages. (4)

9) With so many choices no wonder these diagrams branch off in so many directions. (4)

DOWN

2) Adding it up as you go along. (10)

3) It's not the height but the area of each bar that matters with this type of chart. (9)

4) Distance from the lowest to highest. (5)

6) Sand dart deviation? (8)

8) Perhaps the most common way of finding an average. (4)

5.1   Questions on Straight Lines

Keep learning these straight lines till they start coming out of your ears — you've got to know about the *vertical/horizontal* lines and the *sloping* ones *through the origin*.

Q1   Make a copy of this diagram:

a) Label the x axis.
b) Label the y axis.
c) Draw the line x = 3.
d) Draw the line y = 2.
e) Draw and label the line x + y = 0.
f) Draw and label the line x – y = 0.

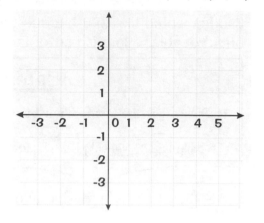

Q2   Make a copy of this diagram:

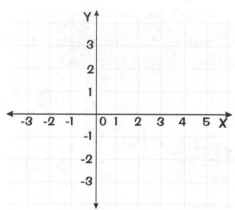

a) Label the line x = 0.
b) Label the line y = 0.
c) Draw and label the line y = x.
d) Draw and label the line y = –x.
e) Draw the line x = –3.
f) Draw the line y = –2.

Q3   Which letters represent the following lines:

a) x = y
b) x = 5
c) y = –x
d) x = 0
e) y = –7
f) x + y = 0
g) y = 5
h) x – y = 0
i) y = 0
j) x = –7?

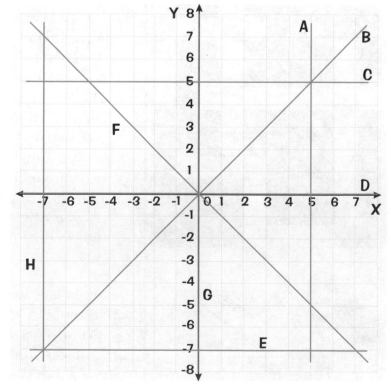

Don't get confused if you've got "x + y = ... " — just rearrange the equation to "y = -x + ..." and as if by magic, you've got a line you recognise.

5.2 Questions on Plotting Straight Lines

Q1 Complete the following table for the line y = 3x − 1:

X	-4	-3	-2	-1	0	1	2	3	4
3x									
-1									
y									

Plot these points on graph paper and hence draw the graph of y = 3x − 1. Use a scale of 1 cm for 2 units on the y axis and 2 cm for 1 unit on the x axis.

Q2 Complete the following table for the line y = 2x − 2:

X	-4	-3	-2	-1	0	1	2	3	4
2x									
-2									
y									

Plot these points on graph paper and hence draw the graph of y = 2x − 2.

Q3 Complete the following table for the line y = ½x − 3:

x	-6	-4	-2	0	2	4	6
½ x							
-3							
y							

Plot these points on graph paper and hence draw the graph of y = ½x − 3.

Q4 Complete the following table for the line y = ¼x − 4:

x	-8	-4	0	4	8	12	16
¼ x							
-4							
y							

Plot these points on graph paper and hence draw the graph of y = ¼x − 4.

To plot a straight line, the **very first thing** you've got to do is work out a **table of values**, then once you know they're in a straight line, just get your ruler out and you're away.

5.2   *Questions on Plotting Straight Lines*

Q5   Complete this table of values
for $y = 2x + 3$:

X	0	3	8
y			

Plot these points on graph paper and
draw the graph of $y = 2x + 3$.
Use your graph to find:

a) The value of y when x = 5
b) The value of y when x = 2
c) The value of x when y = 11
d) The value of x when y = 17

Q6   Complete this table of values
for $y = ¼x - 3$:

X	-8	-4	8
y			

Plot these points on graph paper and
draw the graph of $y = ¼x - 3$.
Use your graph to find:

a) The value of y when x = 2
b) The value of y when x = 0
c) The value of x when y = −2
d) The value of x when y = −1.5

Q7   Complete the following table for
the line $y = -x + 3$.

X	-4	2	6
y			

Plot these points on graph paper and
draw the graph of $y = -x + 3$.
Use your graph to find:

a) The value of y when x = 4
b) The value of y when x = 1
c) The value of x when y = 2
d) The value of x when y = 5

Q8   Complete the following table for
the line $y = -2x + 4$.

X	-4	0	4
y			

Plot these points on graph paper and
draw the graph of $y = -2x + 4$.
Use your graph to find:

a) The value of y when x = 3
b) The value of y when x = −1
c) The value of x when y = 10
d) The value of x when y = −2

Q9   Complete the following table for
the line $y = -\dfrac{x}{5} + 3$.

X	-10	-4	10
y			

Plot these points on graph paper and
draw the graph of $y = -\dfrac{x}{5} + 3$.
Use your graph to find:

a) The value of y when x = −7
b) The value of y when x = −1
c) The value of x when y = 3.6
d) The value of x when y = 2

Q10   Complete the following table for
the line $y = -\dfrac{x}{4} - 2$.

X	-12	-6	6
y			

Plot these points on graph paper and
draw the graph of $y = -\dfrac{x}{4} - 2$.
Use your graph to find:

a) The value of y when x = −4
b) The value of y when x = −1
c) The value of x when y = −2.75
d) The value of x when y = 0

SECTION FIVE — GRAPHS

5.2   Questions on Plotting Straight Lines

Q11   The cost of hiring a car is calculated using the formula:
Total cost = £25 + 20p for each kilometre travelled.
Copy and complete this table:

Number of kilometres	0	50	100	200	300	350
Total cost in £						

Plot these points on a graph (put distance travelled on the horizontal axis and total cost on the vertical axis). Use your graph to find the cost of hiring the car when the following distances have been travelled:

a) 170 km

b) 270 km

c) 320 km.

Use your graph to find the number of kilometres travelled when this total cost is:

d) £78

e) £34

f) £42.

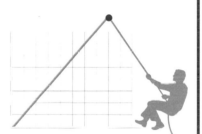

Q12   The cost of electricity is calculated using the formula:
Total cost = Fixed charge + cost per unit.

Customers can choose two different methods of payment:
Method A: Fixed charge £10, cost per unit 25p
Method B: Fixed charge £40, cost per unit 5p
Copy and complete this table:

Number of Units used	0	100	200	300
Cost using method A				
Cost using method B				

Plot these points on a graph (put the number of units on the horizontal axis, cost on the vertical axis):

a) Use your graph to find the total cost when 70 units are used for:
   i) Method A
   ii) Method B

b) Miss Wright used 75 units. Which method should she use to minimize her bill, Method A or Method B?

c) Mr Jones and Mrs Green both used exactly the same number of units and paid the same amount. Mr Jones used Method A, Mrs Green used Method B. How many units did they each use?

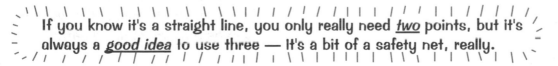

If you know it's a straight line, you only really need *two* points, but it's always a *good idea* to use three — It's a bit of a safety net, really.

5.3 Questions on Y = mX + C

This is a really nifty way of finding the gradient and y-intercept — you really do need to know it because it'll save you loads of time. Anything for an easy life...

Q1 What is the gradient of:

a) line A
b) line B
c) line C
d) line D
e) line E
f) line F
g) line G
h) line H
i) line I
j) line J?

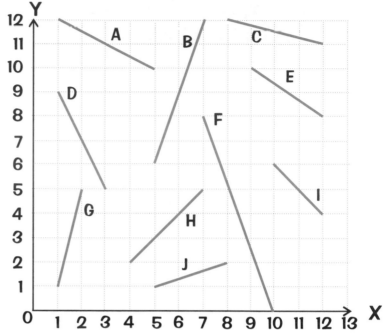

I know these are a bit more algebra-ish, but don't worry, they won't bite.

Q2 For each of the following lines, give the gradient and the coordinates of the point where the line cuts the y-axis.

a) $y = 4x + 3$
b) $y = 3x - 2$
c) $y = 2x + 1$
d) $y = -3x + 3$
e) $y = 5x$
f) $y = -2x + 3$
g) $y = -6x - 4$
h) $y = x$
i) $y = -\frac{1}{2}x + 3$
j) $y = \frac{1}{4}x + 2$
k) $3y = 4x + 6$

l) $2y = -5x - 4$
m) $8y = 4x - 12$
n) $3y = 7x + 5$
o) $x + y = 0$
p) $x - y = 0$
q) $y - x = 3$
r) $x - 3 = y$
s) $y - 7 = 3x$
t) $y - 5x = 3$
u) $y + 2x + 3 = 0$
v) $y - 2x - 4 = 0$

Q3 What is the gradient of the lines joining the points:
a) (3, 5) and (5, 9)
b) (6, 3) and (10, 5)
c) (−6, 4) and (−3, 1)
d) (8, 2) and (4, 10)
e) (8, 5) and (6, 4)
f) (−3, −1) and (1, −4)?

Uphill gradients are always positive, downhill always negative. Impressed? Hmmm....thought not. Can be a bit of an uphill battle, these.

SECTION FIVE — GRAPHS

5.3 Questions on Y = mX + C

Q4 Find the equation of the following lines:
a) A
b) B
c) C
d) D
e) E
f) F

Yeah, OK, this sounds a bit scary, but just work out the gradient (m) and look at the y-intercept (c) and pop them back into "y = mx + c"... easy lemons.

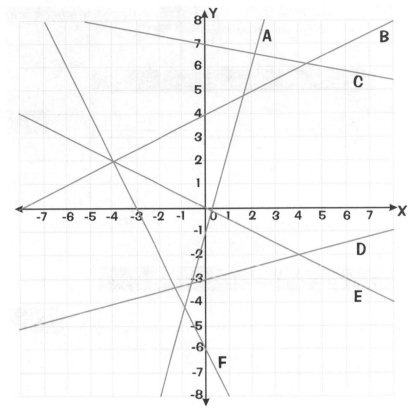

Q5 Find the equation of the straight line which passes through:
a) (3, 7) and has a gradient of 1
b) (2, 8) and has a gradient of 3
c) (–3, 3) and has a gradient of 2
d) (4, –4) and has a gradient of –1
e) (–1, 7) and has a gradient of –3
f) (4, –11) and has a gradient of –2.

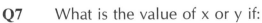
Here's a bit more practice with those gradients. Thought you'd like that.

Q6 Write down the equation of the line which passes through the points:
a) (2, 2) and (5, 5)
b) (1, 3) and (4, 12)
c) (–2, –3) and (5, 11)
d) (1, 0) and (5, –12)
e) (–5, 6) and (–1, –2)
f) (4, 23) and (–2, –7).

Q7 What is the value of x or y if:
a) the point (x, 13) is on the line y = 3x + 1
b) the point (x, –2) is on the line y = ½x – 6
c) the point (4, y) is on the line y = 2x – 1
d) the point (–3, y) is on the line y = –3x?

Q8 Which of the following points lie on the line y = 3x – 1?
(7, 20), (6, 15), (5, 14)

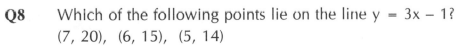

5.4   *Questions on Plotting Curves*

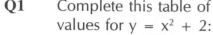

In case you hadn't noticed, it's always a good idea to put *lots of steps* in the *table of values* — that way it's *easier to check* any points that look wrong.

Q1 Complete this table of values for $y = x^2 + 2$:

x	-3	-2	-1	0	1	2	3
x^2							
+2							
y							

Draw the graph of $y = x^2 + 2$

Q2 Complete this table of values for $y = 2x^2 - 4$:

x	-3	-2	-1	0	1	2	3
$2x^2$							
-4							
y							

Draw the graph of $y = 2x^2 - 4$

Q3 Complete this table of values for $y = -x^2 + 2$:

x	-3	-2	-1	0	1	2	3
$-x^2$							
+2							
y							

Draw the graph of $y = -x^2 + 2$

Q4 Complete this table of values for $y = -2x^2 + 6$:

x	-3	-2	-1	0	1	2	3
$-2x^2$							
+6							
y							

Draw the graph of $y = -2x^2 + 6$

Q5 Complete this table of values for $y = x^3$:

x	-3	-2	-1	0	1	2	3
$y=x^3$							

Draw the graph of $y = x^3$

Q6 Complete this table of values for $y = -x^3$:

x	-3	-2	-1	0	1	2	3
$y=-x^3$							

Draw the graph of $y = -x^3$

Q7 Complete this table of values for $y = x^3 + 4$:

x	-3	-2	-1	0	1	2	3
x^3							
+4							
Y							

Draw the graph of $y = x^3 + 4$

Q8 Complete this table of values for $y = -x^3 - 4$:

x	-3	-2	-1	0	1	2	3
$-x^3$							
-4							
y							

Draw the graph of $y = -x^3 - 4$

Q9 Look at your graphs for questions 5 and 7. What has been done to graph 5 to change it into graph 7? Without plotting a table of values draw the graph of $y = x^3 - 4$.

Q10 Look at your graphs for questions 6 and 8. What has been done to graph 6 to change it into graph 8? Without plotting a table of values draw the graph of $y = -x^3 + 4$.

5.5   Questions on Solving Eq's Using Graphs

Q1   Use the graph to solve the following simultaneous equations:

a) $y - 3x = -7$ and $y + x = 9$
b) $y - 3x = -7$ and $3y - x = 3$
c) $y + x = 9$ and $3y - x = 3$

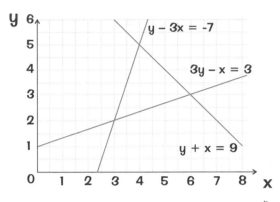

This is a nice _easy way_ of solving simultaneous equations. All you've got to be able to do is draw two straight line graphs and read off a value where they _cross each other_. Does mean you've got to be up to speed with your straight line graphs, though...

Q2

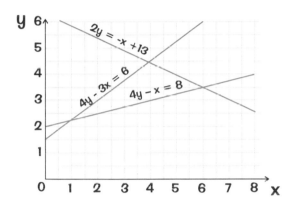

Use the graph to solve the following simultaneous equations:

a) $4y - x = 8$ and $4y - 3x = 6$
b) $4y - x = 8$ and $2y = -x + 13$

Q3   Use the graph to solve the following simultaneous equations:

a) $2y - x = 2$
   $y + x = 4$
b) $2y - x = 2$
   $2y + x = -6$

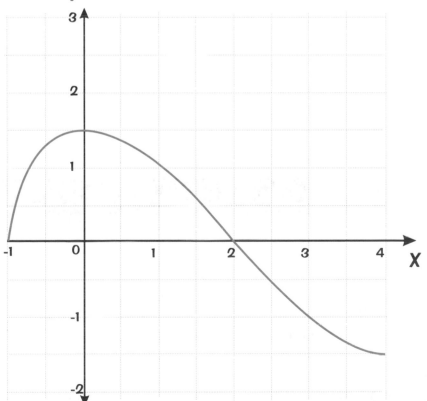

5.5 Questions on Solving Eq's Using Graphs

Q4 Solve the following simultaneous equations by drawing graphs. Use values $0 \leqslant x \leqslant 6$

a) $y = x$
   $y = 9 - 2x$

b) $y = 2x + 1$
   $2y = 8 + x$

c) $y = 4 - 2x$
   $x + y = 3$

d) $y = 3 - x$
   $3x + y = 5$

e) $2x + y = 6$
   $y = 3x + 1$

f) $y = 2x$
   $y = x + 1$

g) $x + y = 5$
   $2x - 1 = y$

h) $2y = 3x$
   $y = x + 1$

i) $y = x - 3$
   $y + x = 7$

j) $y = x + 1$
   $2x + y = 10$

Q5 The diagram shows the graphs:
   $y = x^2 - x$
   $y = x + 2$
   $y = 8$
   $y = -2x + 4$

Use the graphs to find the solutions to:

a) $x^2 - x = 0$

b) $x^2 - x = x + 2$

c) $x^2 - x = 8$

d) $x^2 - x = -2x + 4$

e) $-2x + 4 = x + 2$

f) $x^2 - x - 8 = 0$

g) $x^2 + x = 4$

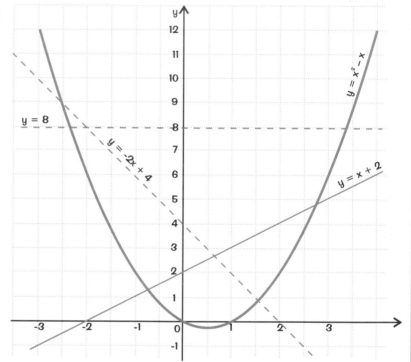

These equations look a bit nasty, but they're just made up of the equations you've got graphs for. And you know how to do the rest of it, don't you...

Q6 Complete this table for $y = x^2 - 4$:

X	-4	-3	-2	-1	0	1	2	3	4
x^2									
-4									
y									

Draw the graph $y = x^2 - 4$
Use your graph to solve the following equations (to 1 d.p.):

a) $x^2 - 4 = 1$

b) $x^2 - 4 = 0$

c) $x^2 - 4 = x$

5.5   Questions on Solving Eq's Using Graphs

Q7   Complete this table for $y = -\frac{1}{2}x^2 + 5$

x	-4	-3	-2	-1	0	1	2	3	4
$-\frac{1}{2}x^2$									
+5									
y									

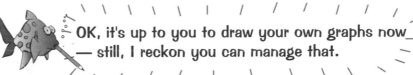

Draw the graph $y = -\frac{1}{2}x^2 + 5$
Use your graph to solve the following equations (to 1 d.p.):

a) $-\frac{1}{2}x^2 + 5 = 0$

b) $-\frac{1}{2}x^2 + 5 = -3$

c) $-\frac{1}{2}x^2 + 5 = x$

OK, it's up to you to draw your own graphs now — still, I reckon you can manage that.

Q8   Use graphical methods to solve the following equations:

a) $x^2 + 3x = -2$ (use VALUES $-4 \leqslant x \leqslant 2$)

b) $x^2 - 6 = x$ (use VALUES $-4 \leqslant x \leqslant 4$)

c) $x^2 + 2 = x + 4$ (use VALUES $-4 \leqslant x \leqslant 4$)

d) $x^2 + 7x = -12$ (use VALUES $-5 \leqslant x \leqslant 0$)

e) $x^2 - 4 = -3x$ (use VALUES $-5 \leqslant x \leqslant 2$)

f) $x^2 - 4x = -3$ (use VALUES $0 \leqslant x \leqslant 5$)

g) $2x^2 + 5x = -2$ (use VALUES $-3 \leqslant x \leqslant 0$)

h) $x^2 + 3x = x + 4$ (use VALUES $-4 \leqslant x \leqslant 4$)

Q9   An object starts from a point O and moves in a straight line so that at time t seconds its displacement from O is d metres. Its equation is given by $d = \frac{1}{2}t(5 - t)$.

a) Complete the following table:

t	0	1	2	2.5	3	4	5	6
$\frac{1}{2}t$								
(5 - t)								
$d = \frac{1}{2}t(5 - t)$								

b) Draw a graph to show values for t from 0 to 6 on the horizontal scale using a scale of 2 cm to 1 second. Use a scale of 2 cm to 1 metre for values of d on the vertical scale.

c) Use your graph to answer the following questions:

  i) After how many seconds does the object return to O?

  ii) What was its greatest distance from O during the 6 seconds?

  iii) After how many seconds was the object at its greatest distance from O?

  iv) After how many seconds was the object 1 metre from O?
  (give your answer to 1 d.p.)

118

5.6 Questions on Tangents and Gradient

Q1 This is the graph of $y = x^2$

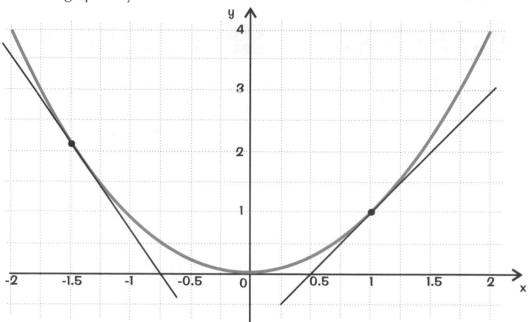

Tangents to the curve have been drawn at $x = 1$ and $x = -1.5$. Use these tangents to calculate the gradient of the curve at:

a) $x = 1$

b) $x = -1.5$.

\ \ \ \ \ \ | / / / / / / /
Well, this is just more gradients, isn't it... a tangent to the curve at a certain point has the same gradient as the curve has at that point. Well, it would, wouldn't it...
/ / / / / | \ \ \ \ \ \

Q2 This is the graph of $y = x^2 + 3x$.

Tangents to the curve have been drawn at $x = 1$ and $x = -2$.

Use these tangents to calculate the gradient of the curve at:

a) $x = 1$

b) $x = -2$.

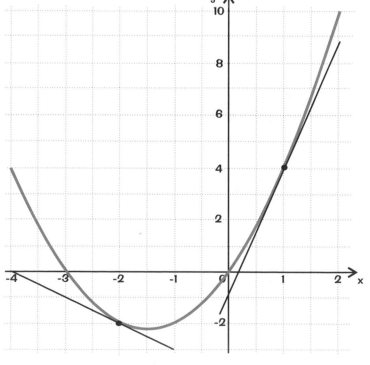

SECTION FIVE — GRAPHS

5.6   Questions on Tangents and Gradient

Q3   Complete this table for the curve $y = \frac{1}{2}x^2 - 3$

X	-3	-2	-1	0	1	2	3
$\frac{1}{2}x^2$							
-3							
y							

Draw the curve for the values $-3 \leqslant x \leqslant 3$. Find the gradient of the curve at:

a) x = −2

b) x = 1.

c) What is the value of x when the gradient is 0?

Make sure you draw *really smooth* curves — so you get your tangent *more accurate*... and your answer *more right* (more importantly).

Q4   Complete this table for the curve $y = x^2 - 5x$

X	-3	-2	-1	0	1	2	3
x^2							
-5x							
y							

Draw the curve for the values $-3 \leqslant x \leqslant 3$. Find the gradient of the curve at:

a) x = 2

b) x = 0

c) x = 1.

d) What is the value of x when the gradient is 0?

Q5   Complete this table for the curve $y = x^2 + 3x - 2$

X	-3	-2	-1	0	1	2	3
x^2							
+3x							
-2							
y							

Draw the curve for the values $-3 \leqslant x \leqslant 3$. Find the gradient of the curve at:

a) x = 2

b) x = −1

c) x = 1.

d) What is the value of x when the gradient is 0?

5.6 Questions on Tangents and Gradient

Q6   A stone is thrown into the air. This graph shows the height of the stone against time.
By drawing tangents estimate the speed of the stone after:

a) 3 seconds
b) 5 seconds.

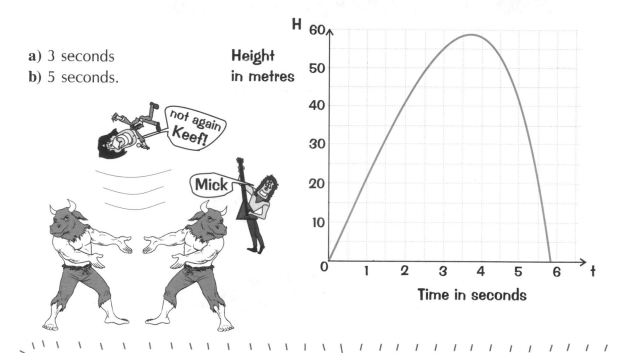

Don't get your tangents in a muddle... if there's more than one tangent, use *different colours* — and at least it'll brighten up an otherwise dull evening of Maths homework.

Q7   A rocket is fired vertically. It reaches its maximum height then returns to the ground.
By drawing tangents estimate the speed of the rocket after:

a) 2 seconds
b) 3 seconds
c) 5 seconds.

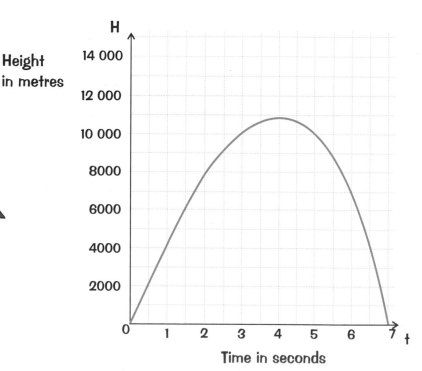

5.7 Questions on Graphs to Recognise

Q1 Identify the type of graph shown below. Choose from straight line, quadratic, cubic and reciprocal:

a)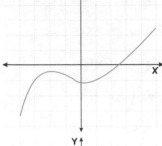

b)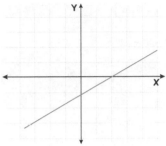

c)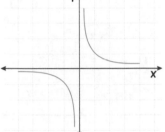

d)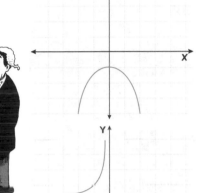

e)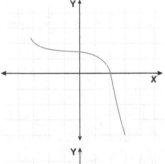

f)

g)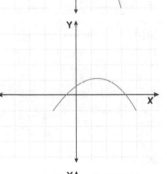

h)

i)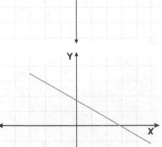

j)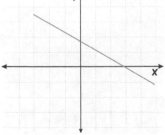

k)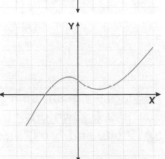

l)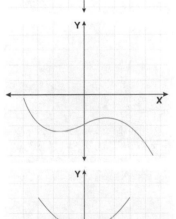

5.7 Questions on Graphs to Recognise

Q2 Here are some equations, and there are some curves below. Match the equations to the curves on this page and the following page.

a) $y = 3x + 1$

b) $y = 4x - 1$

c) $y = -2x - 1$

d) $y = 3^x$

e) $y = -2x$

f) $y = 3x$

g) $y = -x^2$

h) $y = x^2 + 2$

i) $y = x^2 - 3$

j) $y = -x^2 + 3$

k) $y = -x^2 - 3$

l) $y = x^2$

m) $y = x^3 + 3$

n) $y = 2x^3 - 3$

o) $y = -\frac{1}{2}x^3 + 2$

p) $y = -x^3 + 3$

q) $y = x^3$

r) $y = -\frac{3}{x}$

s) $y = \frac{2}{x}$

t) $y = \frac{1}{x^2}$

u) $y = -\frac{1}{x^2}$

i)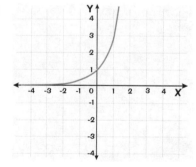

ii)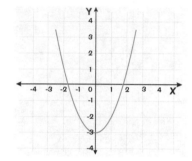

iii)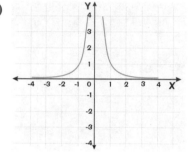

iv)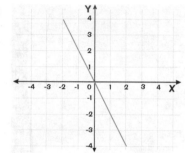

v)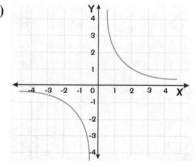

vi)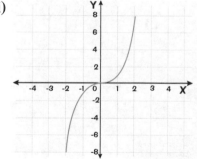

vii)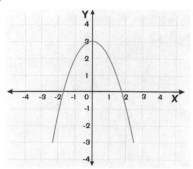

viii)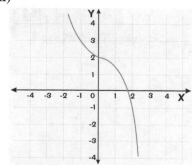

ix)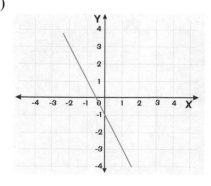

You'll need to be able to _sketch a graph_ from _memory_ — yeah, scary huh. Don't worry — they only expect you to remember the **5 main ones** (phew) — _straight_ line (easy), $\underline{x^2}$ (buckets), $\underline{x^3}$ (wiggly), $\underline{1/x}$ (2 bits and "x=0" missing) and k^x (that tricky curve up through (0,1))

5.7 *Questions on Graphs to Recognise*

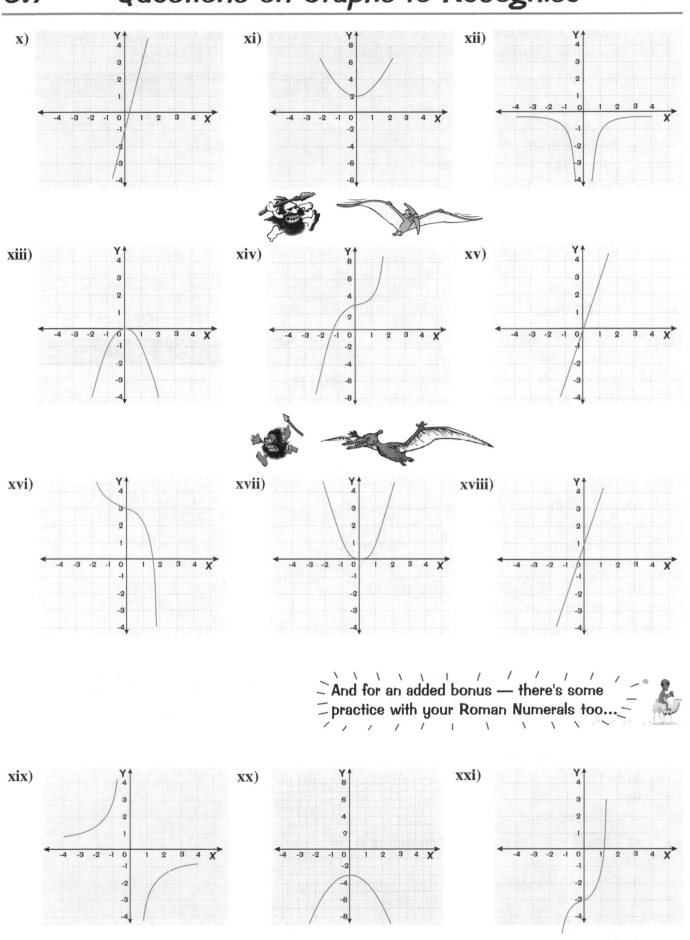

x)

xi)

xii)

xiii)

xiv)

xv)

xvi)

xvii)

xviii)

And for an added bonus — there's some practice with your Roman Numerals too...

xix)

xx)

xxi)

124

5.8   Questions on Equations from Graphs

Make sure you know the what the four main curves look like, and what their equations are — then you've just got to find the two unknowns and stick 'em back in.

Q1   The table shows the price of electricity.

Number of units used	100	200	300	500
Price (£)	8	11	14	20

Plot the points on a graph with the number of units used on the horizontal axis and the price (£) on the vertical axis.

a) Find a formula connecting price (P) and number of units (N) used.

b) Use your formula to calculate the price of:
   i) 400 units
   ii) 700 units.

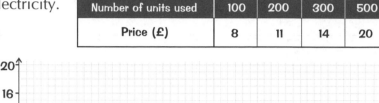

Q2   The table shows the labour costs of having a television repaired. The cost consists of a fixed rate call-out charge plus a charge for each ten minutes.

Time (min)	10	20	30	40	50
Cost (£)	8	10		14	16

Plot the points on a graph with the time on the horizontal axis and the cost on the vertical axis.

a) Find a formula correcting the cost (C) in pounds and the time (M) in minutes.

b) What is the fixed rate call-out charge?

c) Use your graph to find the cost for 30 minutes.

d) Use your formula to find this cost for:
   i) 80 minutes
   ii) 100 minutes
   iii) 3 hours.

Q3   Two variables x and y are connected by the equation y = mx + c.

x	1	3	5	8
y	9	17	25	37

Draw a graph with x on the horizontal axis and y on the vertical axis. Use your graph to find the value of:

a) m
b) c
   — and hence:
c) write down the equation connecting x and y.

d) Use your equation to find the value of y when:
   i) x = 6
   ii) x = 10

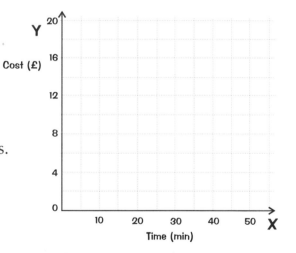
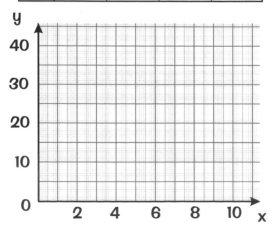

SECTION FIVE — GRAPHS

5.8   Questions on Equations from Graphs

Q4   Two variables x and y are connected by the equation $y = ax^2 + b$.

Here are some values of x and y.

x	2	3	4	5
y	5	7.5	11	15.5

Draw a graph plotting x^2 on the horizontal axis using a scale of 1 cm to 2 units and y on the vertical using a scale of 1 cm to 1 unit.

Use your graph to find:
a) the value of a
b) the value of b.
c) Write down the equation connecting x and y.

Q5   Two variables x and y are connected by the equation $y = ax^2 + b$.

Here are some values of x and y.

x	1	2	3	4
y	-1	5	15	29

Draw a graph plotting x^2 on the horizontal axis using a scale of 1 cm to 1 unit and y on the vertical using a scale of 1 cm to 2 units.

Use your graph to find:
a) the value of a
b) the value of b.
c) Write down the equation connecting x and y.

Q6   Two variables A and B are connected by the equation $A = mB^2 + c$.

Here are some values of A and B.

B	1	2	3	4
A	10.25	11	12.25	14

Choose suitable scales and draw a graph plotting B^2 on the horizontal axis and A on the vertical axis.
Use your graph to find:
a) the value of m
b) the value of c.
c) Write down the equation connecting A and B.

Q7   Two variables C and D are connected by the equation $C = aD^3 + b$.

Here are some values of C and D.

D	1	2	2.5	3
C	-4	3	10.625	22

Choose suitable scales and draw a graph plotting D^3 on the horizontal axis and C on the vertical axis. Use your graph to find:
a) the value of a
b) the value of b.
c) Write down the equation connecting C and D.

They could give you any of the 4 main curves — squared, cubic, exponential or trig. Be warned...

SECTION FIVE — GRAPHS

5.8   Questions on Equations from Graphs

Q8   In an experiment the measurements of two variables A and B were taken.

The values are shown in this table.

A	1	1.5	2	2.5	3
B	2.8	3.7	4.9	5.9	6.7

A and B are connected by the equation $B = mA + c$.
Plot the values obtained in the experiment on a graph. Plot A on the horizontal axis and B on the vertical axis. Draw a line of best fit and hence find the values of:

a) m
b) c.
c) Write down the equation connecting A and B.

Q9   In an experiment the measurements of two variables P and Q were taken.

The values are shown in this table.

P	0.5	1	1.5	2	2.5
Q	3.3	4.7	6.3	8.1	9.2

P and Q are connected by the equation $Q = aP + b$.
Plot the values obtained in the experiment on a graph. Plot P on the horizontal axis and Q on the vertical axis. Draw a line of best fit and hence find the values of:

a) a
b) b.
c) Write down the equation connecting P and Q.

Q10   Two variables A and B are connected by the equation $B = mA^3 + c$.

Here are some values of A and B.

A	1	2	3	4	5
B	-10	-3	16	51	117

Choose suitable scales and draw a suitable graph (plot A on the vertical axis).
Draw a line of best fit. Use your graph to find the value of:

a) m
b) c.
c) Write down the equation connecting A and B.

Q11   Two variables C and D are connected by the equation $D = aC^n + b$. The value of n is known to be either 2 or 3.

Here are some values of C and D.

C	1	2	3	4	5
D	10.5	12	14.5	18	22.5

Choose suitable scales and draw a suitable graph (plot C on the vertical axis).
Use your graph to find the value of:

a) a
b) b
c) n.
d) Write down the equation connecting C and D.

SECTION FIVE — GRAPHS

5.9 Questions on Area

Q1 This is a speed-time graph of a train journey.

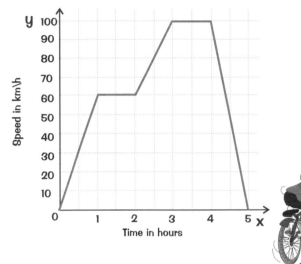

a) Calculate the distance travelled in:
  i) The first two hours.
  ii) The last two hours.
b) Calculate the total distance travelled.

Q2 This is a speed-time graph of a cycle ride.

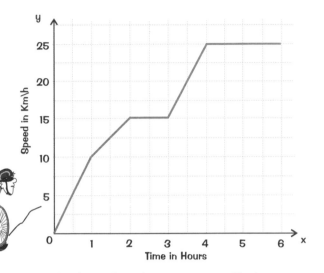

a) Calculate the distance travelled in:
  i) The first two hours.
  ii) The last two hours.
b) Calculate the total distance travelled.

 Add up all the little trapezia to find the whole area — easy trapeasy...

Q3 This graph shows the speed of a train during a period of six seconds.

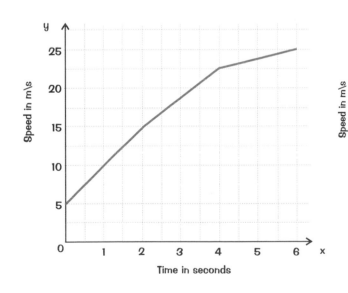

Estimate the total distance travelled in the period of six seconds by dividing the area into three trapeziums of equal width.

Q4 This graph shows the speed of a train during a period of eight seconds.

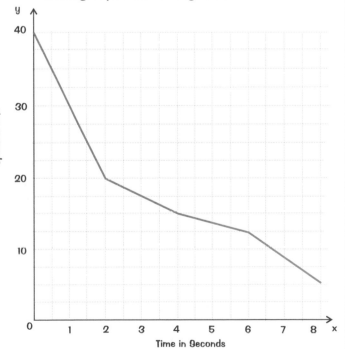

Estimate the total distance travelled in the period of eight seconds by dividing the area into four trapeziums of equal width.

SECTION FIVE — GRAPHS

5.10   *Questions on Linear Programming*

Q1   Copy and complete this diagram to show the inequalities:

$y > 1, x > 2, x + y < 6$

Shade the region which satisfies all of the inequalities.

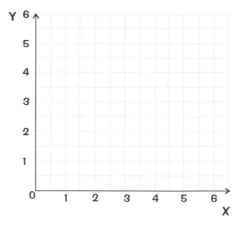

 It can get confusing when you're trying to work out which side of each line to shade. Instead of rushing in with a guess, always check with a *coordinate* first.

Q2   Copy and complete this diagram to show the inequalities:

$y > 0, x > 0, 3x + 4y \leqslant 12$

Shade the region which satisfies all of the inequalities.

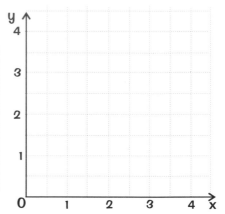

The *easiest* coordinate to try is *(0,0)*, but you can't use it if it's on any of the lines, so try something like *(1,0)*, *(0,1)* or *(1,1)* — it's always best to keep it *simple*.

Q3   Copy and complete this diagram to show the inequalities:

$2x + 3y \leqslant 12, x \geqslant 0, y \geqslant 0, 2x + 3y \geqslant 6$

Shade the region which satisfies all of the inequalities.

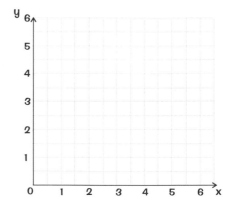

Q4   Copy and complete this diagram to show the inequalities:

$x > 1, x < 6, y > 0, x > y$

Shade the region which satisfies all of the inequalities.

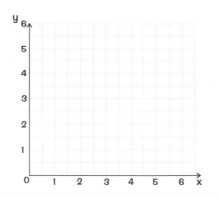

5.10   Questions on Linear Programming

Q5   Describe the shaded region using inequalities.

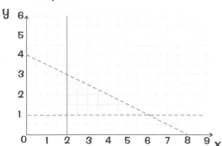

Q6   Describe the shaded region using inequalities.

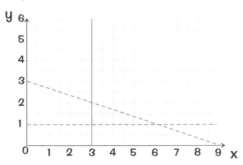

Q7   Describe the shaded region using inequalities.

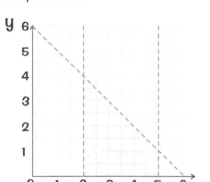

Q8   Describe the shaded region using inequalities.

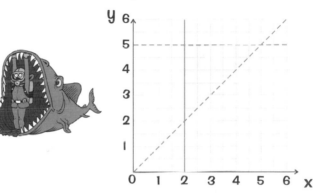

  These are just the same as the last page, but back-to-front... all you've got to do is work out the equations — and you were only doing that a mere 3 pages ago.

Q9   Sarah has a maximum of £100 to spend on books and CD's. Books cost £5 each, CD's cost £10 each. She must buy more CD's than books. She must buy at least 5 books.

a) Write three inequalities to show her constraints.

b) Draw a linear programme graph to show these inequalities. Put books (B) on the horizontal axis and CD's (C) on the vertical axis.

c) Shade the region which satisfies these inequalities.

d) Write down all of the solutions which satisfy these inequalities.

Q10   Mr Smith has a maximum of £10,000 to spend on machinery. He has a choice of two machines. <u>Machine A</u> costs £200, <u>machine B</u> costs £500, and he must buy at least 40 machines.

a) Write two inequalities to describe his constraints.

b) Draw a linear programme graph to show these inequalities. Put machine A on the horizontal axis and machine B on the vertical axis.

c) Shade the region which satisfies these inequalities.

d) Machine A produces 4 items per day, machine B produces 11 items per day. Mr Smith wants to maximise output.

   i) How many machines of type A should he purchase?

   ii) How many machines of type B should he purchase?

   iii) What is the maximum number of items which can be produced in a day?

5.11 Questions on Transforming Graphs

Q1 This is a graph of y = f(x).

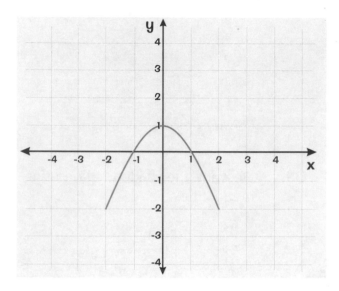

Use the graph of y = f(x) to sketch:
a) y = f(x) + 3
b) y = f(x) − 3
c) y = f(x + 3)
d) y = f(x − 3)
e) y = -f(x)
f) y = f(2x)
g) y = f(½x)
h) y = −f(2x)

You've got to learn about these _shifts_ and _stretches_ — there are _only 4_, so it won't take long. If you don't, either you'll have to _spend ages_ working it out, or worse still you'll _have to guess_. Seems a bit of a waste of time _and marks_ to me...

Q2 This is a graph of y = f(x).

Use the graph of y = f(x) to sketch:
a) y = f(x) + 2
b) y = f(x) − 2
c) y = f(x + 2)
d) y = f(x − 2)
e) y = −f(x)
f) y = f(2x)
g) y = f(½x)
h) y = f(x + 3) − 1
i) y = f(x − 1) + 3

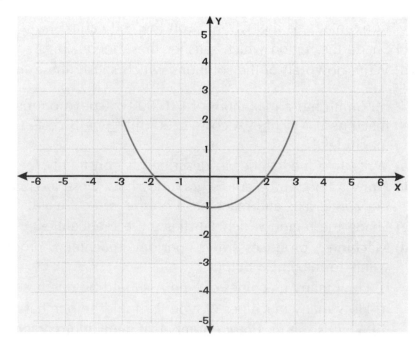

131

5.11 Questions on Transforming Graphs

Q3 This is the graph of y = sin(x)

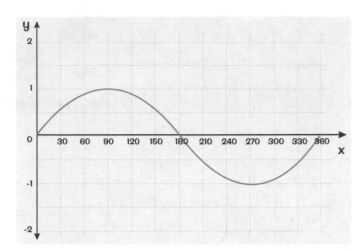

Draw the graph of:
a) y = 2sin(x)
b) y = sin(2x).

Q4 This is the graph of y = cos(x)

Draw the graph of:
a) y = 2cos(x)
b) y = cos(2x).

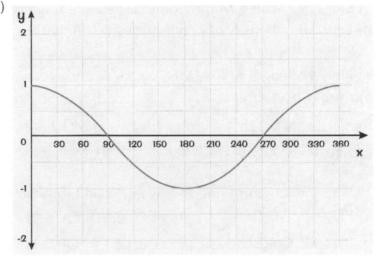

Q5 This is the graph of Y = f(X)
Sketch the graphs of:

a) Y = f(X) + 1
b) Y = −f(X)
c) Y = f(X + 1)
d) Y = f(½X)
e) Y = f(2X)
f) Y = 2f(X)
g) Y = f(X + 1) − 2.

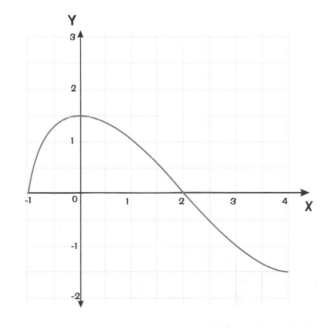

Phew — well, that's the lot on graphs... and what fun it was, too.

5.12 Questions on Uses of Coordinates

Q1 Find the midpoint of the line AB, where A and B have coordinates:

a) A(2,3) B(4,5)

b) A(1,8) B(10,2)

c) A(0,11) B(11,11)

d) A(3,15) B(14,3)

e) A(6,7) B(0,0)

f) A(16,16) B(3,3)

g) A(8,33) B(32,50)

h) A(17,28) B(44,13)

ahh... nice'n'easy...

Q2 Find the midpoints of each of these lines:

a) Line PQ, where P has coordinates (−1,5) and Q has coordinates (5,6).

b) Line AB, where A has coordinates (−3,3) and B has coordinates (4,0).

c) Line RS, where R has coordinates (4,−5) and S has coordinates (0,0).

d) Line PQ, where P has coordinates (−1,−3) and Q has coordinates (3,1).

e) Line GH, where G has coordinates (10,13) and H has coordinates (−6,−7).

f) Line CD, where C has coordinates (−4,6) and D has coordinates (12,−7).

g) Line MN, where M has coordinates (−5,−8) and N has coordinates (−21,−17).

h) Line AB, where A has coordinates (−1,0) and B has coordinates (−9,−14).

Q3 Find the length of line MN, where M and N have coordinates:

a) M(6,3) N(2,8)

b) M(1,5) N(8,12)

c) M(0,1) N(7,3)

d) M(9,5) N(4,8)

e) M(10,4) N(10,0)

f) M(12,6) N(13,0)

Q4 Find the length of line PQ, where P and Q have coordinates:

a) P(2,−3) Q(3,0)

b) P(1,−8) Q(4,3)

c) P(0,−1) Q(2,−3)

d) P(1,−4) Q(−2,7)

e) P(−6,−1) Q(7,−9)

f) P(12,−3) Q(−5,5)

g) P(−10,−2) Q(−2,−8)

h) P(−5,2) Q(2,−5)

OK, so there's a few negative numbers creeping in here, but they're really no harder.

Q5 For each of the lines on this graph, find:
(i) the midpoint and
(ii) the length.

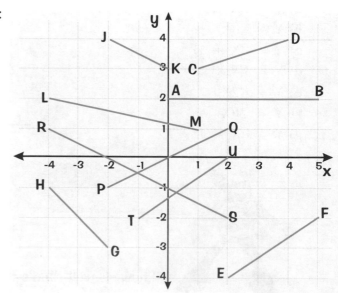

6.1   Questions on The Basics

Q1   Work out the following temperature changes:
   a) 20°C to -7°C   **c)** -17°C to -5°C   **e)** -31°C to -16°C
   b) -10°C to -32°C   **d)** -3°C to 15°C   **f)** -5°C to -17°C

Q2   Which is larger and by how much?
   a) -12 + 7 − 4 + 6 − 2 + 7 or **b)** -30 + 26 − 3 − 7 + 17

Q3   A Roman soldier was born in 17BC and died in the year AD29. How old was he when he died?

Q4   Simplify   **a)** $4x − 5x + 3x − x + 2x − 7x$ **b)** $30y − 10y + 2y − 3y + 4y − 5y$

Q5   Find the value of xy and $\frac{x}{y}$ for each of the following:
   a) $x = -100$ $y = 10$ **c)** $x = -48$ $y = -3$
   b) $x = 24$ $y = -4$ **d)** $x = 0$ $y = -4$

Q6   Find the value of $(a − b) \div (c + d)$ when $a = 10$, $b = −26$, $c = −5$ and $d = −4$.

Q7   Simplify the following:
   a) $2x \times -3y$ **d)** $4p \times -4p$ **g)** $10x \div - 2y$ **j)** $70x^2 \div -7x^2$
   b) $-8a \times 2b$ **e)** $-30x \div -3y$ **h)** $-30x \div -10x$ **k)** $-36x^2 \div -9x$
   c) $-4x \times -2x$ **f)** $50x \div -5y$ **i)** $40ab \div -10ab$ **l)** $40y^2 \div -5y$

Q8   Using the fact that $a^2 − b^2 = (a + b)(a − b)$, factorise the following expressions:
   a) $x^2 − 9$ **d)** $36 − a^2$ **g)** $25 − 16z^2$ **j)** $x^4 − y^4$
   b) $y^2 − 16$ **e)** $4x^2 − 9$ **h)** $1 − 36a^2$ **k)** $1 − (ab)^2$
   c) $25 − z^2$ **f)** $9y^2 − 4$ **i)** $x^4 − 36$ **l)** $100 x^2 − 144y^2$

Q9   Simplify the following by collecting like terms together:
   a) $3x^2 + 4x + 12x^2 − 5x$ **f)** $15ab − 10a + b − 7a + 2ba$
   b) $14x^2 − 10x − x^2 + 5x$ **g)** $4pq − 14p − 8q + p − q + 8p$
   c) $12 − 4x^2 + 10x − 3x^2 + 2x$ **h)** $13x^2 + 4x^2 − 5y^2 + y^2 − x^2$
   d) $20abc + 12ab + 10bac + 4bc$ **i)** $11ab + 2cd − ba − 13dc + abc$
   e) $8pq + 7p + q + 10qp − q + p$ **j)** $3x^2 + 4xy + 2y^2 − z^2 + 2xy − y^2 − 5x^2$

Q10   Multiply out the brackets and simplify where possible:
   a) $4(x + y − z)$ **h)** $14(2m − n) + 2(3n − 6m)$ **o)** $x^2(x + 1)$
   b) $x(x + 5)$ **i)** $4x(x + 2) − 2x(3 − x)$
   c) $−3(x − 2)$ **j)** $3(2 + ab) + 5(1 − ab)$ **p)** $4x^2\left(x + 2 + \frac{1}{x}\right)$
   d) $7(a + b) + 2(a + b)$ **k)** $(x − 2y)z − 2x(x + z)$
   e) $3(a + 2b) − 2(2a + b)$ **l)** $4(x − 2y) − (5 + x − 2y)$ **q)** $8ab(a + 3 + b)$
   f) $4(x − 2) − 2(x − 1)$ **m)** $a − 4(a + b)$ **r)** $7pq\left(p + q − \frac{1}{p}\right)$
   g) $4e(e + 2f) + 2f(e − f)$ **n)** $4 pq(2 + r) + 5qr(2p + 7)$ **s)** $4\big[(x + y) − 3(y − x)\big]$

Q11   For each of the large rectangles below, write down the area of each of the small rectangles and hence find an expression for the area of each large rectangle.

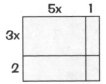

6.1   *Questions on The Basics*

*Remember **FOIL** for multiplying brackets... don't want to miss any terms now, do you...*

Q12   Multiply out the brackets and simplify your answers where possible:

a) $(x - 3)(x + 1)$ e) $(x + 2)(x - 7)$ i) $(x - 3)(4x + 1)$

b) $(x - 3)(x + 5)$ f) $(4 - x)(7 - x)$ j) $2(2x + y)(x - 2y)$

c) $(x + 10)(x + 3)$ g) $(2 + 3x)(3x - 1)$ k) $4(x + 2y)(3x - 2y)$

d) $(x - 5)(x - 2)$ h) $(3x + 2)(2x - 4)$ l) $(3x + 2y)^2$

Q13   Find the product of $5x - 2$ and $3x + 2$.

Q14   Find the square of $2x - 1$.

Q15   A rectangular pond has length $(3x - 2)$ m and width $(5 - x)$ m. Write down a simplified expression for:

a) the pond's perimeter   b) the pond's area.

Q16   A rectangular bar of chocolate consists of 20 small rectangular pieces. The size of a small rectangular piece of chocolate is 2 cm by x cm.

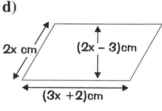

a) Write down an expression for the perimeter of the whole bar.

b) Write down an expression for the area of the whole bar.

c) If I ate 6 small rectangular pieces of chocolate, what is the area of the remaining piece?

Q17   Find a simplified expression for the perimeter *and* the area of the following shapes.

a)   b)   c)   d)

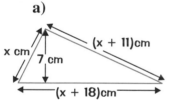 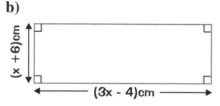 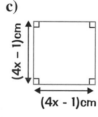 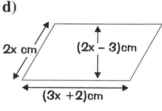

Q18   All the expressions below have a^2 as a common factor. Factorise each of them.

a) $a^2b + a^2c$ d) $a^3 + a^2y$

b) $5a^2 + 13a^2b$ e) $2a^2x + 3a^2y + 4a^2z$

c) $2a^2b + 3a^2c$ f) $a^2b^2 + a^3c^2$

Q19   Each term below has $4xyz$ as a common factor. Factorise each of them.

a) $4xyz + 8xyz$ b) $8xyz + 12xyz$ c) $8xyz + 16x^2yz$ d) $20x^2y^2z^2 + 16xyz^2$

Q20   Factorise:

a) $16x - 28$ d) $x^2 + 4x^2 + 2x$ g) $p^3 + p^4$

b) $4^2 - 14y$ e) $8b^3 + 16y^2 + 32t + 8$ h) $2ab^2 - 6a^2b^2 + 18abc$

c) $3q^2 - 12q$ f) $x^2y^2 - 3xy$ i) $xy - y^2x + x^2y + x^2y^2$

Q21   Factorise:

a) $7a^2bc^2 + 14ab^2c + 21ab^2c^2 + 28a^2b^2c^2$

b) $100x^2yz + 90x^3yz + 80x^2y^2z + 70x^2yz + 60x^2yz^2$

Q22   Factorise:

Hmm, that last one looks a bit tricky — have a think about multiplying out brackets like at the top of the page.

a) $x^2 - 4$ b) $144 - y^4$ c) $1 - 9x^2y^2$ d) $49x^4y^4 - 1$

6.2   Questions on Algebraic Fractions

The trick for doing <u>algebraic fractions</u> is remembering how to do <u>normal fractions</u> — because they're <u>just the same</u>... in fact you can see at a glance if there's an x on the top <u>and</u> the bottom, so I reckon they're probably <u>even easier</u>.

Q1   Simplify the following by cancelling down where possible:

a) $\dfrac{27x^4y^2z}{9x^3yz^2}$
    b) $\dfrac{48a^2b^2}{(2a)^2c}$
    c) $\dfrac{3xyz}{9x^2y^3z^4}$
    d) $\dfrac{4p^3q^3}{(2pr)^3}$

Q2   Multiply out the following, leaving your answer as simplified as possible:

a) $\dfrac{x^2}{y} \times \dfrac{2}{x^3}$
    e) $\dfrac{10z^3}{xy} \times \dfrac{4x^3}{5z}$
    i) $\dfrac{5a^2b}{b} \times \dfrac{3a^2c^3}{10bd}$

b) $\dfrac{3a^4}{2} \times \dfrac{b}{a^2}$
    f) $\dfrac{30a^2b^2c^2}{7} \times \dfrac{21c^2}{ab^3}$
    j) $\dfrac{p^2}{pq^2} \times \dfrac{q^2}{p}$

c) $\dfrac{2x}{y^2} \times \dfrac{y^3}{4x^3}$
    g) $\dfrac{4}{x} \times \dfrac{x^3}{2} \times \dfrac{x}{10}$
    k) $\dfrac{90r^2}{14t} \times \dfrac{7t^3}{30r}$

d) $\dfrac{3pq}{2} \times \dfrac{4r^2}{9p}$
    h) $\dfrac{2a^2}{3} \times \dfrac{9b}{a} \times \dfrac{2a^2b}{5}$
    l) $\dfrac{400d^4}{51e^5} \times \dfrac{102d^2e^4}{800e^2f}$

Q3   Divide the following, leaving your answer as simplified as possible:

a) $\dfrac{4x^3}{y} \div \dfrac{2x}{y^2}$
    e) $\dfrac{e^2f^2}{5} \div \dfrac{ef}{10}$
    i) $\dfrac{25a^3}{b^3} \div \dfrac{5}{b^2}$

b) $\dfrac{ab}{c} \div \dfrac{b}{c}$
    f) $\dfrac{5x^3}{y} \div \dfrac{1}{y}$
    j) $\dfrac{4x}{y^4z^4} \div \dfrac{2}{y^2z^3}$

c) $\dfrac{30x^3}{y^2} \div \dfrac{10x}{y}$
    g) $\dfrac{16xyz}{3} \div \dfrac{4x^2}{9}$
    k) $\dfrac{3m}{2n^2} \div \dfrac{m}{4n}$

d) $\dfrac{pq}{r} \div \dfrac{2}{r}$
    h) $\dfrac{20a^3}{b^3} \div \dfrac{5}{b^2}$
    l) $\dfrac{70f^3}{g} \div \dfrac{10f^4}{g^2}$

Q4   Solve the following equations for x:

a) $\dfrac{20x^4y^2z^3}{7xy^5} \times \dfrac{14y^3}{40x^2z^3} = 5$
    b) $\dfrac{48x^5y^2}{12z^3} \div \dfrac{16x^2y^2}{z^3} = 2$

SECTION SIX — LOVELY ALGEBRA

6.2 *Questions on Algebraic Fractions*

OK, I guess it gets a bit tricky here — you've got to cross-multiply to get a common denominator before you can get anywhere with adding or subtracting.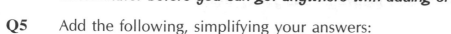

Q5 Add the following, simplifying your answers:

a) $\dfrac{3}{2x} + \dfrac{y}{2x}$

b) $\dfrac{1}{x} + \dfrac{y}{x}$

c) $\dfrac{4xy}{3z} + \dfrac{2xy}{3z}$

d) $\dfrac{(4x+2)}{3} + \dfrac{(2x-1)}{3}$

e) $\dfrac{5x+2}{x} + \dfrac{2x+4}{x}$

f) $\dfrac{6x}{3} + \dfrac{2x+y}{6}$

g) $\dfrac{x}{8} + \dfrac{2+y}{24}$

h) $\dfrac{x}{10} + \dfrac{y-1}{5}$

i) $\dfrac{2x}{3} + \dfrac{2x}{4}$

j) $\dfrac{x}{6} + \dfrac{5x}{7}$

k) $\dfrac{x}{3} + \dfrac{x}{y}$

l) $\dfrac{zx}{4} + \dfrac{x+z}{y}$

Q6 Subtract the following, leaving your answer as simplified as possible:

a) $\dfrac{4x}{3} - \dfrac{5y}{3}$

b) $\dfrac{4x+3}{y} - \dfrac{4}{y}$

c) $\dfrac{(8x+3y)}{2x} - \dfrac{(4x+2)}{2x}$

d) $\dfrac{(9-5x)}{3x} - \dfrac{(3+x)}{3x}$

e) $\dfrac{10+x^2}{4x} - \dfrac{x^2+11}{4x}$

f) $\dfrac{2x}{3} - \dfrac{y}{6}$

g) $\dfrac{z}{5} - \dfrac{2z}{15}$

h) $\dfrac{4m}{n} - \dfrac{m}{3}$

i) $\dfrac{2b}{a} - \dfrac{b}{7}$

j) $\dfrac{(p+q)}{2} - \dfrac{3p}{5}$

k) $\dfrac{p-2q}{4} - \dfrac{2p+q}{2}$

l) $\dfrac{3x}{y} - \dfrac{4-x}{3}$

Q7 Simplify the following:

a) $\left(\dfrac{a}{b} \div \dfrac{c}{d}\right) \times \dfrac{ac}{bd}$

b) $\dfrac{x^2+xy}{x} \times \dfrac{z}{xz+yz}$

c) $\dfrac{(p+q)}{r} \times \dfrac{3}{2(p+q)}$

d) $\dfrac{m^2n}{p} + \dfrac{mn}{p^2}$

e) $\dfrac{1}{x+y} + \dfrac{1}{x-y}$

f) $\dfrac{2}{x} - \dfrac{3}{2x} + \dfrac{4}{3x}$

g) $\dfrac{a+b}{a-b} + \dfrac{a-b}{a+b}$

h) $\dfrac{1}{4pq} \div \dfrac{1}{3pq}$

i) $\dfrac{x}{8} - \dfrac{x+y}{4} + \dfrac{x-y}{2}$

6.3   *Questions on Solving Equations*

Q1   When 1 is added to a number and the answer then trebled, it gives the same result as doubling the number and then adding 4. Find the number.

Q2   Solve the following:

   a) $2x^2 = 18$ b) $2x^2 = 72$ c) $3x^2 = 27$ d) $4x^2 = 36$ e) $5x^2 = 5$

Q3   Solve the following:

   a) $3x + 1 = 2x + 6$ c) $5x - 1 = 3x + 19$ e) $x + 15 = 4x$
   b) $4x + 3 = 3x + 7$ d) $\frac{1}{2}x + 2 = x - 1$ f) $3x^2 + 3 = 2x^2 + 12$

Q4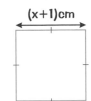
(x+1)cm

A square has sides of length $(x + 1)$ cm. Find the value of x if:

   a) the perimeter of the square is 66 cm
   b) the perimeter of the square is 152.8 cm.

Q5   Solve the following:

   a) $3x - 8 = 7$ d) $2x - 9 = 25$ f) $5x - 2 = 6x - 7$
   b) $2(x - 3) = -2$
   c) $4(2x - 1) = 60$ e) $\frac{24}{x} + 2 = 6$ g) $30 - \frac{x^2}{2} = 28$

Q6   Mary is y years old. Her father is 4 times older than Mary. Her mother is 7 years younger than her father. If their three ages add up to 101 years, find the value of y. Find the ages of Mary's parents.

Q7   Mr Smith sent his car to the local garage. He spent £x on new parts, four times this amount on labour and finally £29 for an MOT test. If the total bill was for £106.50, find the value of x.

Q8   Solve:

   a) $2(x - 3) - (x - 2) = 5$ g) $\frac{x}{3} + 7 = 12$ j) $41 - \frac{x}{11} = 35$
   b) $5(x + 2) - 3(x - 5) = 29$
   c) $2(x + 2) + 3(x + 4) = 31$ h) $\frac{x}{10} + 18 = 29$ k) $\frac{x}{100} - 3 = 4$
   d) $10(x + 3) - 4(x - 2) = 7(x + 5)$
   e) $5(4x + 3) = 4(7x - 5) + 3(9 - 2x)$ i) $17 - \frac{x^2}{3} = 5$ l) $\frac{120}{x} = 16$
   f) $3(7 + 2x) + 2(1 - x) = 19$

Q9   Joan, Kate and Linda win £2,400 on the National Lottery between them. Joan gets a share of £x, whilst Kate gets twice as much as Joan. Linda's share is £232 less than Joan's amount.

   a) Write down an expression for the amounts Joan, Kate and Linda win.
   b) Write down an expression in terms of x, and solve it.
   c) Write down the amounts Kate and Linda receive.

Q10   All the angles in the diagram are right angles.

   a) Write down an expression for the perimeter of the shape.
   b) Write down an expression for the area of the shape.
   c) For what value of x will the perimeter and area be numerically equal?

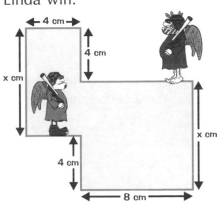

Big blobs and broomsticks...

6.3   *Questions on Solving Equations*

Q11   Solve the following:

a) $5(x - 1) + 3(x - 4) = -11$

b) $3(x + 2) + 2(x - 4) = x - 3(x + 3)$

c) $\dfrac{3x}{2} + 3 = x$

d) $3(4x + 2) = 2(2x - 1)$

e) $\dfrac{5x + 7}{9} = 3$

f) $\dfrac{2x + 7}{11} = 3$

Q12   Two men are decorating a room. One has painted 20 m² and the other only 6 m². They continue painting and both manage to paint another x m² each. If the first man has painted exactly three times the area painted by the second man, find the value of x.

It's easy — you just put the 2 bits together and there's your equation. Then all you've got to do is solve it...

Q13   For what value of x is the expression $14 - \dfrac{x}{2}$ equal to the value $\dfrac{3x - 4}{2}$?

Q14   Carol's father was 24 years old when Carol was born. Now he is four times as old as Carol. How old is Carol?

Q15   Mr Jones is 4 years older than his wife and 31 years older than his son. Their ages add up to 82 years. If Mr Jones is x years old, find the value of x and find the age of his wife and son.

Q16   Solve the following:

a) $\dfrac{y}{2} + 2 = 13$

b) $\dfrac{3x}{4} - 2 = 4$

c) $\dfrac{2z}{5} - 3 = -5$

d) $\dfrac{1}{5}(x - 4) = 3$

e) $\dfrac{2}{3}(x + 1) = 16$

f) $\dfrac{3}{5}(4x - 3) = 15$

g) $\dfrac{8}{x^2} = \dfrac{32}{36}$

h) $\dfrac{12}{5x^2} = \dfrac{3}{20}$

i) $\dfrac{14}{3x^2} = \dfrac{2}{21}$

Q17   A train travels at 70 mph for x hours and then at 80 mph for $(\dfrac{x}{2} + 3)$ hours.

If the train covers 405 miles of track, find the value of x.

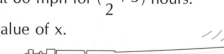

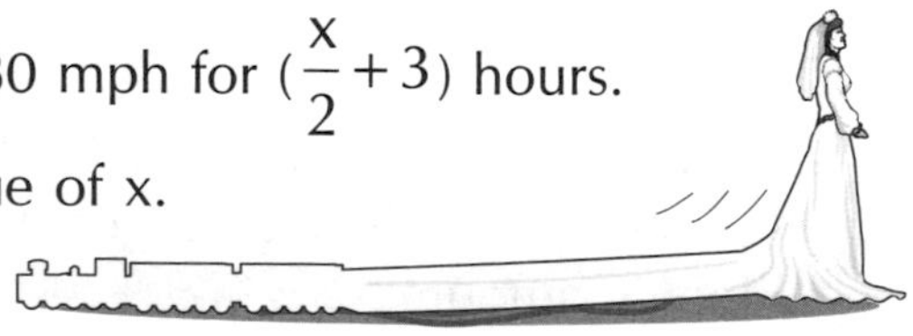

Q18   Solve the following:

a) $\dfrac{4x + 3}{2} + x = \dfrac{5x + 41}{4}$

b) $\dfrac{5}{7}(x - 2) - \dfrac{3}{4}(x + 3) = -4$

Q19   A triangle has lengths as shown below. Find the length of each side, if the length of AC exceeds that of AB by ½ cm.

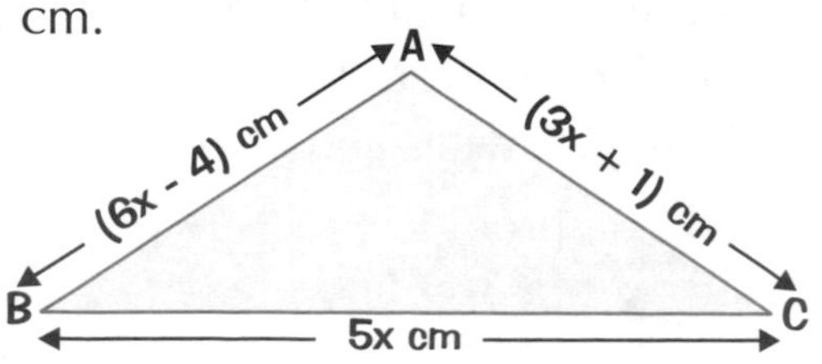

(6x - 4) cm   A   (3x + 1) cm

B   5x cm   C

6.4   Questions on Rearranging Formulas

 Rearranging is getting the letter you want out of the formula and making it the subject. And it's exactly the same method as for solving equations, which can't be bad.

Q1   Rearrange the following formulas to make the letter in brackets the new subject.

a) $g = 10 - 4h$ (h)

b) $d = \frac{1}{2}(c + 4)$ (c)

c) $j = -2(3 - k)$ (k)

d) $a = \dfrac{2b}{3}$ (b)

e) $f = \dfrac{3g}{8}$ (g)

f) $y = \dfrac{x}{2} - 3$ (x)

g) $s = \dfrac{t}{6} + 10$ (t)

h) $p = 4q^2$ (q)

Q2   A car salesperson is paid £w for working m months and selling c cars, where
$$W = 500m + 50c$$

a) Rearrange the formula to make c the subject.

b) Find the number of cars the salesperson sells in 11 months if he earns £12,100 during that time.

Q3   The cost of hiring a car is £28 per day plus 25p per mile.

a) Find the cost of hiring the car and travelling:

   i) 40 miles.

   ii) 80 miles.

b) Write down a formula to give the cost of hiring a car (£) for one day, and travelling n miles.

c) Rearrange the formula to make n the subject.

d) How many miles can you travel, during one day, if you have a budget of:

   i) £34, ii) £50,   iii) £56.50.

Q4   Rearrange the following formulas to make the letter in brackets the new subject.

a) $y = x^2 - 2$ (x)

b) $y = \sqrt{(x + 3)}$ (x)

c) $r = \left(\dfrac{s}{2}\right)^2$ (s)

d) $f = \dfrac{10 + g}{3}$ (g)

e) $w = \dfrac{5 - z}{2}$ (z)

f) $v = \frac{1}{3}x^2 h$ (x)

g) $v^2 = u^2 + 2as$ (a)

h) $v^2 = u^2 + 2as$ (u)

i) $t = 2\pi\sqrt{\frac{l}{g}}$ (g)

Q5   Mrs Smith buys x jumpers for £J each and sells them in her shop for a total price of £T.

a) Write down an expression for the amount of money she paid for all the jumpers.

b) Using your answer to **a)**, write down a formula for the profit £P Mrs Smith makes selling all the jumpers.

c) Rearrange the formula to make J the subject.

d) Given that Mrs Smith makes a profit of £156 by selling 13 jumpers for a total of £364 find the price she paid for each jumper originally.

6.4 Questions on Rearranging Formulas

Q6 The cost of developing a film is 12p per print plus 60p postage.

a) Find the cost of developing a film with:

    i) 12 prints.

    ii) 24 prints.

b) Write down a formula for the cost C, in pence, of developing x prints.

c) Rearrange the formula to make x the subject.

d) Find the number of prints developed when a customer is charged:

    i) £4.92

    ii) £6.36

    iii) £12.12.

Q7 Rearrange the following formulas, by collecting terms in x and looking for common factors, to make x the new subject.

a) $xy = z - 2x$ **e)** $xy = xz - 2$

b) $ax = 3x + b$ **f)** $2(x - y) = z(x + 3)$

c) $4x - y = xz$ **g)** $xyz = x - y - wz$

d) $xy = 3z - 5x + y$ **h)** $3y(x + z) = y(2z - x)$

Q8 Rearrange the following to make the letter in brackets the new subject.

a) $pq = 3p + 4r - 2q$ (p)   **g)** $\sqrt{hk^2 - 14} = k$ (k)

b) $fg + 2e = 5 - 2g$ (g)   **h)** $2\sqrt{x} + y = z\sqrt{x} + 4$ (x)

c) $a(b - 2) = c(b + 3)$ (b)   **i)** $\dfrac{a}{b} = \dfrac{1}{3}(b - a)$ (a)

d) $pq^2 = rq^2 + 4$ (q)   **j)** $\dfrac{m + n}{m - n} = \dfrac{3}{4}$ (m)

e) $4(a - b) + c(a - 2) = ad$ (a)   **k)** $\sqrt{\dfrac{(d - e)}{e}} = 7$ (e)

f) $\dfrac{x^2}{3} - y = x^2$ (x)   **l)** $\dfrac{x - 2y}{xy} = 3$ (y)

These are getting quite tricky — you've got to <u>collect like terms</u>, before you can make anything else the subject.

Q9 Rearrange the following formulas to make y the new subject.

a) $x(y - 1) = y$ **c)** $x = \dfrac{y^2 + 1}{2y^2 - 1}$

b) $x(y + 2) = y - 3$ **d)** $x = \dfrac{2y^2 + 1}{3y^2 - 2}$

6.5   Questions on Inequalities

Yet another one of those bits of Maths that looks worse than it is — these are just like equations, really, except for the symbols.

Q1   Write down the inequality represented by each diagram below.

a)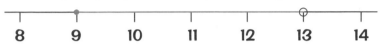

b)

c)

d)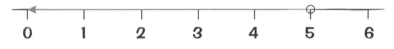

e)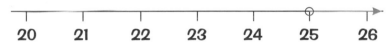

f)

g)

h)

Q2   By drawing an appropriate part of the number line for each question, represent each of the following inequalities.

a) $x > 5$ c) $2 > x > -5$ e) $3 \geqslant x > -2$ g) $-3 \leqslant x \leqslant -2$

b) $x \leqslant 2$ d) $3 > x \geqslant -2$ f) $7 \geqslant x > 6$ h) $0 \geqslant x > -3$

Q3   Draw and label a number line from −5 to 5 for each of the following questions. Represent the inequalities on your number lines.

a) $x^2 \leqslant 4$ c) $x^2 \leqslant 9$ e) $16 \geqslant x^2$ g) $9 > x^2$

b) $x^2 < 1$ d) $25 \geqslant x^2$ f) $x^2 \leqslant 1$ h) $x^2 < 0$

Q4   Solve the following:

a) $3x + 2 > 11$ e) $2x - 7 \geqslant 8$ i) $5(x + 2) \geqslant 25$ m) $8 - 3x \geqslant 14$

b) $5x + 4 < 24$ f) $17 + 4x < 33$ j) $4(x - 1) > 40$ n) $16 - x < 11$

c) $5x + 7 \leqslant 32$ g) $2(x + 3) < 20$ k) $10 - 2x > 4x - 8$ o) $16 - x > 1$

d) $3x + 12 \leqslant 30$ h) $2(5x - 4) < 32$ l) $7 - 2x \leqslant 4x + 10$ p) $12 - 3x \leqslant 18$

SECTION SIX — LOVELY ALGEBRA

6.5 Questions on Inequalities

Q5   There are 1,130 pupils in a school. No class must have more than 32 pupils. How many classrooms could be used? Show this information as an inequality.

Q6   A person is prepared to spend £300 taking friends out to celebrate. If the restaurant charges £12 per head, how many guests could be invited? Show this information as an inequality.

Q7   Find the largest integer x, such that $2x + 5 \geqslant 5x - 2$.

Q8   When a number is subtracted from 11, then divided by two, the result is always less than five. Write this information as an inequality and solve it to show the possible values of the number.

Q9   Each shaded region satisfies three inequalities. Write down the three inequalities.

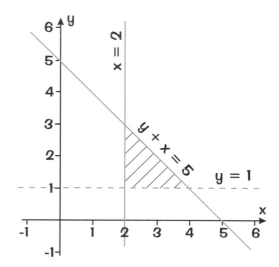

Q10   Draw a set of axes with the x-axis from −2 to 6 and the y-axis from −1 to 7. Show on a graph the region enclosed by the following three inequalities.

$$y < 6 \quad , \quad x + y \geqslant 5 \quad \text{and} \quad x \leqslant 5$$

Q11   Draw a set of axes with the x-axis from 0 to 8 and the y-axis from 0 to 10. Show on a graph the region enclosed by the following three inequalities.

$$x > 1 \quad , \quad x + y \leqslant 7 \quad \text{and} \quad y \geqslant 2$$

Q12   Draw a set of axes with the x-axis from −4 to 5 and the y-axis from −3 to 6. Show on a graph the region enclosed by the following.

$$y \leqslant 2x + 4 \quad , \quad y < 5 - x \quad \text{and} \quad y \geqslant \frac{x}{3} - 1$$

You've seen questions like these before, in Section 5.
For some more practice, turn back there and have
another go at them. Bet you can't wait.

6.6 Questions on Direct & Inverse Proportion

Q1 If 17 textbooks cost £150.45, how much will 28 cost?

Q2 If it takes 4 people 28 hours to complete a task, how long would it take just one person?

Q3 A person earns £6.20 an hour. How much do they earn for 15½ hours work?

Q4 On a map 2 cm represents 3 km.
  a) Two towns are 14 km apart, what is the distance between them on the map?
  b) Two road junctions are 20.3 cm apart on the map, what is their real distance apart?

Q5 y is directly proportional to x. If y = 5 when x is 25, find y when x is 100.

Q6 y is directly proportional to x. If y is 1.2 when x is 2.5, find the value of y when x = 3.75.

Q7 If $y \propto x$ and y = 132 when x = 10, find the value of y when x = 14.

Q8 If $y \propto x$ and y = 117 when x = 45, find the value of x when y = 195.

Q9 Complete the following tables of values where y is always directly proportional to x.

a)

X	2	4	6
Y	5	10	

b)

X	3	6	9
Y		9	

c)

X	27		
Y	5	10	15

Q10 If y = 3 when x = 8 and y is inversely proportional to x, find the value of y when x = 12.

Q11 If $y \propto \dfrac{1}{x}$ and x = 4 when y = 5, find the value of x when y = 10.

Q12 If y and x vary inversely, and y = 12 when x = 3 find:
  a) the value of x when y = 9
  b) the value of y when x = 6.

Q13 A man travels for 2 hours at 72 km per hour, completing a journey between two towns. Meanwhile another man completes the same journey at a speed of 80 km per hour. How long did it take him?

Q14 Given that $y \propto \dfrac{1}{x}$, complete this table of values.

x	1	2	3	4	5	6
y					9.6	

Make sure you know the 4 main details about Direct and Inverse Proportion:
1) what happens when one quantity increases,
2) the graph,
3) the table of values and
4) whether it's the ratio or the product that's the same for all values.

6.6 Questions on Direct & Inverse Proportion

Q15 The area of a circle is proportional to the square of the radius. If the area is 113 cm² when the radius is 6 cm find:
   a) the area of a circle with radius 5 cm
   b) the radius of a circle with area 29 cm³.
   Give your answers to 1 d.p.

Q16 If y is inversely proportional to the square of x, and y = 4 when x = 6.
   Find the value of:
   a) y when x = 3
   b) x when y = 9, given that x is negative.

Q17 If $y \propto x^2$ and y = 4 when x = 4, find the value of y when x = 12.

Q18 $y = kx^3$ and y = 200 when x = 5.
   a) Find the value of k.
   b) Find the value of y when x = 8.
   c) Find the value of x when y = 2433.4

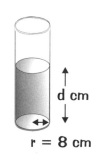

Q19 Given that y varies inversely as the square of x, complete the following table of values, given that x is always positive.

X	1	2	5	
y			4	1

X	2			8
y	24	6	2⅔	

Q20 Two cylindrical containers are filled to the same depth, d cm, with water. The mass of the water in each container is proportional to the square of the radius of each container. The first container has a radius of 16 cm and the water has a mass of 16 kg. If the second container has a radius of 8 cm, find the mass of the water inside it.

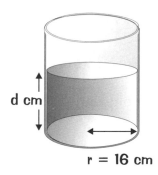

d cm

r = 16 cm

d cm

r = 8 cm

Q21 Given that r varies inversely as the square of s, and r = 24 when s = 10, find the values of:
   a) r when s = 5
   b) s when r = 150, given that s is positive.
   c) r when s = 2
   d) s when r = 37½, given that s is negative.

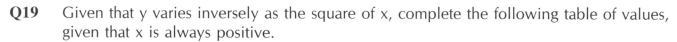
Don't forget about that little joker, the "inverse square" variation — they'll expect you to know that, too.

Q22 By considering the values in the table, decide whether $y \propto x$, $y \propto \dfrac{1}{x}$, $y \propto x^2$ or $y \propto \dfrac{1}{x^2}$.

   a) Write down the equation which shows how y varies with x.
   b) Find the value of y when x = 6.4
   c) Find the value of x when y = 16.

X	1.2	2.5	3.2	4.8
y	166⅔	80	62.5	41⅓

SECTION SIX — LOVELY ALGEBRA

6.7   Questions on Factorising Quadratics

 It's factorising Jim, but not as we know it... Better watch out with these, I reckon.

Q1   Factorise the following:

a) $x^2 + 11x + 24$

b) $x^2 + 15x + 36$

c) $x^2 + 13x + 36$

d) $x^2 + 16x + 48$

e) $x^2 + 14x + 48$

f) $x^2 + 26x + 48$

g) $x^2 + 49x + 48$

h) $x^2 + 19x + 48$

i) $x^2 + 3x$

j) $2x - x^2$

k) $x^2 + 4x$

l) $x^2 - 20x$

m) $x^2 + 10x$

n) $9x + x^2$

o) $x^2 + x - 6$

p) $x^2 - x - 12$

q) $x^2 - 5x + 6$

r) $x^2 - 6x + 8$

s) $x^2 - 11x + 28$

t) $x^2 - 2x - 35$

u) $x^2 - 3x - 40$

v) $x^2 + 10x - 24$

w) $x^2 - 15x + 44$

x) $x^2 - 11x - 26$.

 Your best bet with these is the old guessing game.
Come up with a pair of numbers, then try adding and multiplying them.

Remember, they've got to multiply together to make the number at the
end and add together to make the x term in the middle. Think of FOIL...

Q2   Solve the following quadratic equations:

a) $(x + 2)(x + 8) = 0$

b) $(3 - x)(4 - x) = 0$

c) $(x + 4)(x + 18) = 0$

d) $(x - 2)(x - 2) = 0$

e) $(x + 3)^2 = 0$

f) $(x - 9)^2 = 0$

g) $(x + 4)^2 = 0$

h) $(x - 25)^2 = 0$

i) $x(x + 4) = 0$

j) $x(x - 7) = 0$

k) $x(x + 30) = 0$

l) $x(x + 2) = 0$.

Q3   Factorise the quadratics first, and then solve the equations:

a) $x^2 + 3x - 10 = 0$

b) $x^2 - 5x + 6 = 0$

c) $x^2 - 2x + 1 = 0$

d) $x^2 - 4x + 3 = 0$

e) $x^2 - x - 20 = 0$

f) $x^2 - 4x - 5 = 0$

g) $x^2 + 6x - 7 = 0$

h) $x^2 + 14x + 49 = 0$

i) $x^2 - 2x - 15 = 0$.

Q4   Rearrange into the form "$x^2 + bx + c = 0$", then solve by factorising:

a) $x^2 + 6x = 16$

b) $x^2 + 5x = 36$

c) $x^2 + 4x = 45$

d) $x^2 = 5x$

e) $x^2 = 11x$

f) $x^2 - 21 = 4x$

g) $x^2 - 300 = 20x$

h) $x^2 + 48 = 26x$

i) $x^2 + 36 = 13x$

j) $x + 5 - \dfrac{14}{x} = 0$

k) $x + 4 - \dfrac{21}{x} = 0$

l) $x(x - 3) - 10$

m) $x^2 - 3(x + 6) = 0$

n) $x - \dfrac{63}{x} = 2$

o) $x + 1 = \dfrac{12}{x}$.

6.7　Questions on Factorising Quadratics

Q5　Use "the difference of two squares" to solve these quadratics:

a) $x^2 - 9 = 0$　　　　**c)** $4x^2 - 36 = 0$

b) $x^2 - 16 = 0$　　　　**d)** $9x^2 - 49 = 0$.

Q6　**a)** When x is added to its square, the total is 12. Find the values of x.

b) When y is subtracted from its square, the total is 12. Find the values of y.

Q7　The area of a rectangular swimming pool is 28 m². The width is x m. The difference between the length and width is 3 m. Find the value of x.

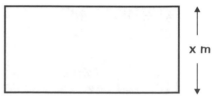

Q8　A rug has length x m. The width is exactly 1 m less than the length.

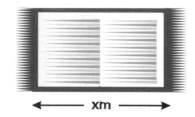

a) Write down an expression for the area of the rug.

b) If the area of the rug is 6 m² find the value of x.

Q9　Solve $x^2 - \frac{1}{4} = 0$.

Q10　A triangle has height (x + 1) cm and a base of 2x cm.

a) Write down an expression for the area of the triangle and simplify it.

b) If the area of the triangle is 12 cm², find the value of x.

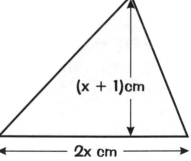

Q11　A square room has a floor of sides x metres. The height of the walls is 3 m. Write down an expression for:

a) the floor area

b) the area of all four walls.

c) If the total area of the floor and the four walls is 64 m² form a quadratic equation and solve it to find x.

Q12　Solve $x + 21 = \dfrac{9(x - 3)}{x}$.

I've seen the sign... when you get any negative numbers in there, look at where the signs are and think about your sign rules for multiplying — it'll help you work out the signs of the numbers you're looking for. Which is bound to save time.

SECTION SIX — LOVELY ALGEBRA

6.8   Questions on The Quadratic Formula

Q1   Find the two values, to 2 d.p, given by each of the following expressions:

a) $\dfrac{2 \pm \sqrt{3}}{2}$

b) $\dfrac{4 \pm \sqrt{10}}{3}$

c) $\dfrac{-2 \pm \sqrt{27}}{2}$

d) $\dfrac{-3 \pm \sqrt{42}}{3}$

e) $\dfrac{-10 \pm \sqrt{160}}{5}$

f) $\dfrac{-27 \pm \sqrt{10}}{2}$

g) $\dfrac{-8 \pm \sqrt{9.5}}{2.4}$

h) $\dfrac{10 \pm \sqrt{88.4}}{23.2}$

Step number 1 on the stairway to spiritual fulfilment... learn the Quadratic Formula.

Q2   The following quadratics can be solved by factorisation, but practise using the formula to solve them.

a) $x^2 + 8x + 12 = 0$
b) $6x^2 - x - 2 = 0$
c) $x^2 - x - 6 = 0$
d) $x^2 - 3x + 2 = 0$
e) $4x^2 - 15x + 9 = 0$
f) $x^2 - 3x = 0$
g) $36x^2 - 48x + 16 = 0$
h) $3x^2 + 8x = 0$
i) $2x^2 - 7x - 4 = 0$

j) $x^2 + x - 20 = 0$
k) $4x^2 + 8x - 12 = 0$
l) $3x^2 - 11x - 20 = 0$
m) $x + 3 = 2x^2$
n) $5 - 3x = 2x^2 = 0$
o) $1 - 5x + 6x^2 = 0$
p) $3(x^2 + 2x) = 9$
q) $x^2 + 4(x - 3) = 0$
r) $x^2 = 2(4 - x)$

Step number 2...
Beware The Minus Signs

Step number 3... divide the whole of the top line by 2a, not just ½ of it
— and remember it's 2a, not just a.

Q3   Solve the following quadratics using the formula. Give your answers to no more than two decimal places.

a) $x^2 + 3x - 1 = 0$
b) $x^2 - 2x - 6 = 0$
c) $x^2 + x - 1 = 0$
d) $x^2 + 6x + 3 = 0$
e) $x^2 + 5x + 2 = 0$
f) $x^2 - x - 1 = 0$
g) $3x^2 + 10x - 8 = 0$

h) $x^2 + 4x + 2 = 0$
i) $x^2 - 6x - 8 = 0$
j) $x^2 - 14x + 11 = 0$
k) $x^2 + 3x - 5 = 0$
l) $7x^2 - 15x + 6 = 0$
m) $2x^2 + 6x - 3 = 0$
n) $2x^2 - 7x + 4 = 0$

Step number 4... check your answers by putting them back in the formula.
So, there you have it — spiritual fulfilment... or as close as you'll get to it within
a 5 mile radius of a quadratic equation.

148

6.8 Questions on The Quadratic Formula

Don't forget FOIL when you multiply out those brackets...

Q4 Rearrange the following in the form "$ax^2 + bx + c = 0$" and then solve by the quadratic formula. Give your answers to two decimal places.

a) $x^2 = 8 - 3x$

b) $(x + 2)^2 - 3 = 0$

c) $3x(x - 1) = 5$

d) $2x(x + 4) = 1$

e) $x^2 = 4(x + 1)$

f) $(2x - 1)^2 = 5$

g) $3x^2 + 2x = 6$

h) $(x + 2)(x + 3) = 5$

i) $(x - 2)(2x - 1) = 3$

j) $2x + \frac{4}{x} = 7$

k) $(x - \frac{1}{2})^2 = \frac{1}{4}$

l) $4x(x - 2) = -3$

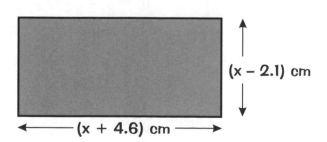 *Pythagoras... remember him — you know, that bloke who didn't like angles.*

Q5 The sides of a right angled triangle are as shown. Use Pythagoras' theorem to form a quadratic equation in x and then solve it to find x.

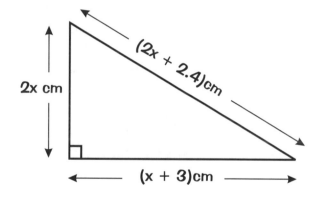

Q6 The area of a rectangle with length $(x + 4.6)$ cm and width $(x - 2.1)$ cm is 134.63 cm².

a) Form a quadratic equation and solve it to find x to two decimal places.

b) What is the rectangle's perimeter to one decimal place?

SECTION SIX — LOVELY ALGEBRA

6.9 Questions on Completing the Square

All you're doing is writing it in the form "(x + 4)² + 2" instead of "x² + 8x + 18" — don't let the name put you off.

Q1 Complete the square for the following expressions:

a) $x^2 - 4x - 5$

b) $x^2 - 2x + 1$

c) $x^2 + x + 1$

d) $x^2 - 6x + 9$

e) $x^2 - 6x + 7$

f) $x^2 - 4x$

g) $x^2 + 3x - 4$

h) $x^2 - x - 3$

i) $x^2 - 10x + 25$

j) $x^2 - 10x$

k) $x^2 + 8x + 17$

l) $x^2 - 12x + 35$

Q2 Solve the following quadratic equations by completing the square. Write down your answers to no more than 2 d.p.

a) $x^2 + 3x - 1 = 0$

b) $x^2 - x - 3 = 0$

c) $x^2 + 4x - 3 = 0$

d) $x^2 + x - 1 = 0$

e) $x^2 - 3x - 5 = 0$

f) $2x^2 - 6x + 1 = 0$

g) $3x^2 - 3x - 2 = 0$

h) $3x^2 - 6x - 1 = 0$

It's quite a cunning method, really... but I admit it takes a bit of getting used to — make sure you've learnt all the steps, then it's just practise, practise...

Algebra Crossword

ACROSS

1 Put brackets in (9)

5 You could do this to an equation (5)

6 There is a formula for this type of equation (9)

9 It goes with improvement (5)

10 Complete this shape (6)

DOWN

1 You should rearrange these (8)

2 x ⩽ –6 is an example of an (10)

3 2x + 4 = 6 is one (8)

4 Some things grow, others _____ (5)

7 It's a type of proportion (7)

8 These are found a lot in algebra (and post boxes) (7)

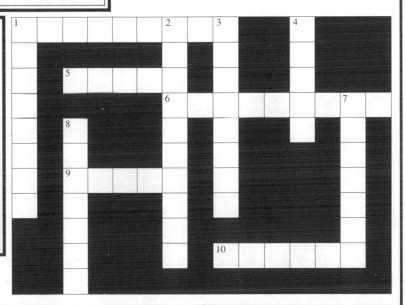

6.10 Questions on Trial and Improvement

Q1   The cubic equation $x^3 + x = 24$ has a solution between 2 and 3. Copy the table below and use it to find this solution to 1 d.p.

Guess(x)	Value of $x^3 + x$	Too large or Too small
2	$2^3 + 2 =$	
3	$3^3 + 3 =$	

Q2   The cubic equation $x^3 - x = 34$ has a solution between 3 and 4. Copy the table below and use it to find this solution to 1.d.p.

Guess(x)	Value of $x^3 - x$	Too large or Too small
3	$3^3 - 3 =$	
4	$4^3 - 4 =$	

Q3   The cubic equation $3x - x^3 = 20$ has a solution between −4 and −3. Copy the table below and use it to find this solution to 1 d.p.

Guess(x)	Value of $3x - x^3$	Too large or Too small
-4	$3(-4) - (-4)^3 = 52$	
-3	$3(-3) - (-3)^3 =$	

Q4   The cubic equation $2x^3 - x = 40$ has a solution between 2 and 3. Copy the table below and use it to find this solution to 1 d.p.

Guess(x)	Value of $2x^3 - x$	Too large or Too small
2	$2(2)^3 - (2) =$	
3	$2(3)^3 - (3) =$	

They don't always give you the starting numbers — so if this happens, make sure you pick two opposite cases (one too big, one too small), or you've blown it.

SECTION SIX — LOVELY ALGEBRA

6.10 Questions on Trial and Improvement

Q5 The cubic equation $x^3 - x^2 = 0.7$ has a solution between 1 and 2. Copy the table on the right and use it to find this solution to 1 d.p.

Guess(x)	Value of $x^3 - x^2$	Too large or Too small
1	$(1)^3 - (1)^2 =$	
2	$(2)^3 - (2)^2 =$	

Q6

Guess(x)	Value of $x^3 - x^2 + x$	Too large or Too small
2	$(2)^3 - (2)^2 + (2) =$	
3	$(3)^3 - (3)^2 + (3) =$	

The cubic equation $x^3 - x^2 + x = 7$ has a solution between 2 and 3. Copy the table on the left and use it to find this solution to 1 d.p.

Q7 The cubic equation $2x^3 + x^2 = 50$ has a solution between 2 and 3. Copy the table on the right and use it to find this solution to 1 d.p.

Guess(x)	Value of $2x^3 + x^2$	Too large or Too small
2	$2(2)^3 + (2)^2 =$	
3	$2(3)^3 + (3)^2 =$	

Q8 The cubic equation $x^3 + x^2 - 4x = 3$ has three solutions. The first solution lies between −3 and −2. The second lies between −1 and 0. The third solution lies between 1 and 2.

Guess(x)	Value of $x^3 + x^2 - 4x$	Too large or Too small
−3	$(-3)^3 + (-3)^2 - 4(-3) = -6$	
−2	$(-2)^3 + (-2)^2 - 4(-2) =$	
−1	$(-1)^3 + (-1)^2 - 4(-1) =$	
0	$(0)^3 + (0)^2 - 4(0) =$	
1	$(1)^3 + (1)^2 - 4(1) =$	
2	$(2)^3 + (2)^2 - 4(2) =$	

The first solution is

.... to 1d.p.

The second solution is

.... to 1d.p.

The third solution is

.... to 1d.p.

Nowt to it really, is there.

152

6.11 Questions on Growth and Decay

Hey look — it's another of those "there is only one formula to learn and you use it for every question" topics.

So I reckon you'd better learn The Formula then...

Q1 Calculate the amount in each account if:
a) £200 is invested for 10 yrs at 9% compound interest per annum
b) £500 is invested for 3 yrs at 7% compound interest per annum
c) £750 is invested for 30 months at 8% compound interest per annum
d) £1000 is invested for 15 months at 6.5% compound interest per annum.

Q2 A colony of bacteria grows at the compound rate of 12% per hour. Initially there are 200 bacteria.
a) How many will there be after 3 hours?
b) How many will there be after 1 day?
c) After how many hours will there be 4000 bacteria? (solve this by trial and error)

Just make sure you get the increase and decrease the right way round... basically, just check your answer sounds like you'd expect — and if it doesn't, do it again.

Q3 A radioactive element was observed every day and the mass remaining was measured. Initially there was 9 kg but this decreased at the compound rate of 3% per day. How much radioactive element will be left after:
a) 3 days
b) 6 days
c) 1 week
d) 4 weeks?
Give your answer to no more than 3 d.p.

Q4 Money is invested on the stock market. During a recession the value of the shares fall by 2% per week.
Find the value of the stock if:
a) £2000 was invested for a fortnight
b) £30,000 was invested for a month
c) £500 was invested for 7 weeks
d) £100,000 was invested for a year.

Q5 Mrs Smith decides to invest £7000 in a saving account. She has the choice of putting all her money into an account paying 5% compound interest per annum or she can put half of her investment into an instant account paying 6% compound interest per annum and the remaining half into an instant access account paying 4% per annum. If she left the investment alone for 3 years, which is her best option and by how much?

 I'd go for Victorian rolling pins, myself...

SECTION SIX — LOVELY ALGEBRA

6.11   Questions on Growth and Decay

Q6   The activity of a radio-isotope decreases at a compound rate of 9% every hour. If the initial activity is recorded at 1100 counts per minute, what will it be after:

a) 2 hours

b) 4 hours

c) 1 day?

d) The activity of the same radio-isotope is recorded at just 65 counts per minute. Using trial and error, estimate the length of time elapsed since the recording of 1100 counts per minute.

Q7   A car is estimated to depreciate in value by 14% each year. Find the estimated values of these used cars:

a) a Peugeot 206 which cost £8,495 six months ago

b) a BMW which cost £34,000 eighteen months ago

c) a Volvo S40 which cost £13,495 two years ago

d) a Vauxhall Vectra which cost £14,395 two years ago

e) a Ford Escort which cost £11,295 three years ago

f) a Daewoo Nexia which cost £6,795 twelve months ago.

Q8   An antique vase has increased in value since its owner bought it five years ago at £220. If its value has appreciated by 16% per year, what value should the owner insure it for today?

Q9   Property prices in one area have depreciated in value by 5% per year. Calculate the expected value today of these properties:

a) a house bought for £45,000 , 3 years ago

b) a bungalow bought for £58,000 , 4 years ago

c) a flat bought for £52,000, six months ago

d) a factory bought for £ 350,000 , 7 years ago.

Q10   A company owns machinery which cost £3,500 four years ago. The depreciation has been 2½% per year. What is the machinery's second-hand value today?

Q11   Bacteria increases in number at a compound rate of 0.4% per hour. If initially there was a culture of 50 cells how many cells will there be after:

a) 3 hours

b) 8 hours 30 minutes

c) 135 mins

d) 2 days?

Q12   The population of a country is 16 million, and the annual compound growth rate is estimated to be 1.3%. Predict the country's population in:

a) 4 years' time

b) 20 years' time.

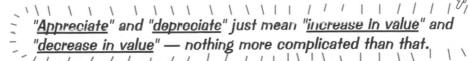

"Appreciate" and "depreciate" just mean "increase in value" and "decrease in value" — nothing more complicated than that.

6.12 Questions on Simultaneous Equations

To solve simultaneous equations from scratch, you've got to get rid of either x or y first — to leave you with an equation with just one unknown in it.

Q1 Eliminate either the x term or the y term by adding or subtracting the pairs of equations and hence solve the equations:

a) $4x - y = 13$
$2x - y = 5$

b) $8x + 3y = 8$
$5x - 3y = 5$

c) $x + 3y = 10$
$2x - 3y = 2$

d) $8x + 6y = 2$
$2(x - 3y) = 3$

e) $x - 12y = 16$
$5x + 12y = 8$

f) $2(5x - y + 4) = 0$
$10x + y = 19$

g) $11x + 3y = 5$
$7x - 3y = 13$

h) $2x + 7y = 11$
$2x + 3y = 7$

i) $x + 6y = 5$
$3(x + 2y - 1) = 0$

Q2 Rearrange the equations before solving for x and y.

a) $3y - 4x = 10$
$4(x - \frac{y}{2} + 2) = 0$

b) $3x + y = 13$
$2y - 3x = 8$

c) $3y + 4x = 10$
$4x - 2y + 8 = 0$

d) $y + 1 = 3x$
$y - x = 3$

e) $y + x = 2$
$y - \frac{1}{2}x + 1 = 0$

f) $y - 3 = 2x$
$y = x - 1$

g) $4y - 3x = 22$
$3x - 2y = -14$

h) $y + 2x = 5$
$y = x - 4$

i) $2y + x = 2$
$y + x + 1 = 0$

j) $3y + 2x = 19$
$2x + y = 1$

k) $9x - y = 12$
$4y - 9x = 6$

l) $6x + 2y = 5$
$3y - 6x = 15$

Q3 Multiply one equation by a number before adding or subtracting. Solve the equations:

a) $3x + 2y = 12$
$2x + y = 7$

b) $5x - y = 17$
$2x + 3y = 0$

c) $x + 3y = 11$
$2x + 5y = 19$

d) $5x + 3y = 24$
$x + 5y = -4$

e) $3x + 2y = 3$
$2x + y = 23$

f) $4x + 2y = 8$
$x + 3y = 2$

g) $x + 14y = -2$
$2x + 3y = 21$

h) $3x + 2y = 21$
$2x - y = 7$

i) $4x - y = -2$
$3x - 2y = 1$

Q4 Multiply both equations by a number before adding or subtracting, to solve these:

a) $7y - 3x = 2$
$5y - 2x = 2$

b) $5x - 8y = 12$
$4x - 7y = 9$

c) $4x - 2y = -6$
$5x + 3y = 20$

d) $7x + 5y = 66$
$3x - 4y = 16$

e) $10x + 4y = 2$
$8x + 3y = 1$

f) $3x + 4y = 19$
$4x - 3y = -8$

Q5 Use the linear equation (the one with no x^2s in it) to find an expression for y. Then substitute it into the quadratic equation (the one <u>with</u> x^2s in it), to solve these equations:

a) $y = x^2 + 2$
$y = x + 14$

b) $y = x^2 - 8$
$y = 3x + 10$

c) $y = 2x^2$
$y = x + 3$

d) $x + 5y = 30$
$x^2 + 4/5x = y$

e) $y = 1 - 13x$
$y = 4x^2 + 4$

f) $y = 3(x^2 + 3)$
$14x + y = 1$

For question 5, you'll get two possible values for x.
Which means you'll also have two possible values for y...

SECTION SIX — LOVELY ALGEBRA

6.12 Questions on Simultaneous Equations

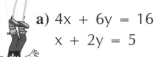

Each time you do a step, <u>write it down</u> — "Multiply A by 2" — that sort of thing. I know it sounds a waste of time, but if you mess it up, it'll be easier to check what went wrong.

Q6 Solve the following simultaneous equations:

a) $4x + 6y = 16$
   $x + 2y = 5$

b) $3x + 8y = 24$
   $x + y = 3$

c) $3y - 8x = 24$
   $3y + 2x = 9$

Careful with parts d) to f) — some of them are quadratics...

d) $y = x^2 - 2$
   $y = 3x + 8$

e) $y = 3x^2 - 10$
   $13x - y = 14$

f) $y + 2 = 2x^2$
   $y + 3x = 0$

g) $3y - 10x - 17 = 0$
   $\frac{1}{3}y + 2x - 5 = 0$

h) $\frac{x}{2} - 2y = 5$
   $12y + x - 2 = 0$

i) $x + y = \frac{1}{2}(y - x)$
   $x + y = 2$

Q7 Two numbers have a sum of 15 and a difference of 3. Write down a pair of simultaneous equations using x and y, and solve them.

Q8 Two numbers have a sum of 4 and a difference of 12. Write down a pair of simultaneous equations using x and y, and solve them.

Q9 A farmer has a choice of buying 6 sheep and 5 pigs for £430 or 4 sheep and 10 pigs for £500 at auction.

a) If sheep cost £x and pigs cost £y, write down his two choices as a pair of simultaneous equations.

b) Solve for x and y.

Q10 Six apples and four oranges cost £1.90, whereas eight apples and two oranges cost £1.80. Find the cost of an apple and the cost of an orange.

Q11 Find the value of x and y for each of the following rectangles, by first writing down a pair of simultaneous equations and then solving them.

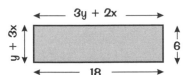
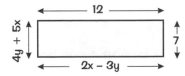
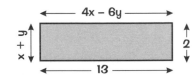

Q12 Two customers enter a shop to buy milk and cornflakes. Mrs Smith buys 5 pints of milk and 2 boxes of cornflakes and spends £3.44. Mr brown buys 4 pints of milk and 3 boxes of cornflakes and receives £6.03 change after paying with a £10 note. Write down a pair of simultaneous equations and solve them to find the price in pence of a pint of milk (m) and a box of cornflakes (c).

Q13 Three pens and seven pencils cost £1.31 whereas eight pencils and six pens cost £1.96. Find the cost of each.

Q14 Solve $\dfrac{3(x - y)}{5} = x - 3y = x - 6$.

6.13 Questions on Simultaneous Eq' Graphs

This is a nice easy way of solving simultaneous equations. All you've got to do is draw 2 straight line graphs and read off a value where they cross each other. It does mean you've got to be up to speed with your straight line graphs, though...

Q1 The simultaneous equations given below have been plotted as straight line graphs. Write down the solutions of the simultaneous equations by looking at the graphs. Finally check your answers by substituting them back into the simultaneous equations.

a) $y + 2x = 9$
$3y = x + 6$

b) $y + x = 1$
$3y = x + 11$

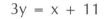

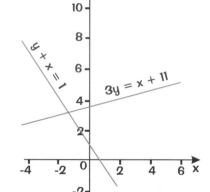

c) $y = 2x - 13$
$2y + x + 6 = 0$

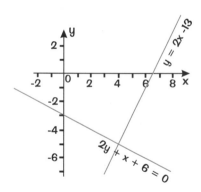

d) $2y = 8 - x$
$2y = x - 2$

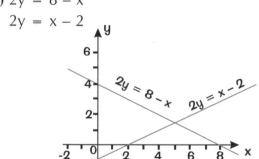

Q2 For each pair of simultaneous equations below:
i) draw and label a pair of axes with x from −3 to 7, and y from −6 to 6
ii) complete two tables of values
iii) plot two straight line graphs onto your axes, remembering to label each graph
iv) use your graphs to find the value of x and y
v) check your answers by substituting them into both of the equations.

a) $y = x + 2$
$y = 3x - 2$

d) $y = x + 3$
$y = 3x - 1$

g) $y = x - 1$
$2y = x + 1$

b) $y = 2x - 2$
$2y = x + 8$

e) $y = 2x + 3$
$y = x - 1$

h) $y + 2 = 4x$
$y + x = 3$

c) $y = x + 1$
$y = 2x - 2$

f) $y = 2 - x$
$y = \frac{1}{2}x - 1$

i) $y + 2 = x$
$y = \frac{1}{2}x + 1$

SECTION SIX — LOVELY ALGEBRA